B. G. F. Dien.

With best wishes

from Lady Townend

1960

FUNGAL DISEASES OF ANIMALS

This and other publications of the Commonwealth Agricultural Bureaux can be obtained through any major bookseller or direct from:
Commonwealth Agricultural Bureaux,
Central Sales, Farnham Royal,
Bucks, England

FUNGAL DISEASES OF ANIMALS

BY

G. C. AINSWORTH, Ph.D., F.L.S.

Commonwealth Mycological Institute,
Kew, Surrey, England

AND

P. K. C. AUSTWICK, B.Sc., F.L.S.

Central Veterinary Laboratory,
Weybridge, Surrey, England

Review Series No. 6 of the
Commonwealth Bureau of Animal Health

COMMONWEALTH AGRICULTURAL BUREAUX
FARNHAM ROYAL · BUCKS · ENGLAND

First Published in 1959
by the
Commonwealth Agricultural Bureaux
Farnham Royal, Bucks, England
20*s*.

Printed by Lithography in Great Britain by
Jarrold & Sons Ltd, Norwich

FOREWORD

Until quite recently the only mycotic diseases which were at all well known to most veterinarians were such conditions as ringworm, aspergillosis in chickens and probably epizootic lymphangitis.

To-day as a result of work in many different countries veterinary mycology is a rapidly growing subject and knowledge of the role of fungi in causing disease in livestock has been greatly increased. Some of these diseases such as mycotic dermatitis in sheep, streptothricosis in cattle and mycotic abortion in cattle are of considerable economic importance, and all of them are of great scientific interest.

The intensive search for new antibiotics produced by fungi which followed the discovery of penicillin has uncovered some substances of great therapeutic value, some with valuable growth-promoting properties but also many which are highly toxic to animals. A by-product of these studies has been a renewed interest in the toxicity of fungus-infested foodstuffs when fed to livestock. Russian workers have been prominent in this field and Sarkisov has published a very useful textbook in the Russian language.

The need for a textbook in English has become apparent and Ainsworth and Austwick have produced a book which will be of great value to practitioners, teachers and students. Both of the authors are well known mycologists who have been in very close touch with veterinary problems, on which one of them has for some time now been wholly employed, and have made considerable original contributions to knowledge on the subject. This dual experience has enabled them to clear up much of the confusion which has existed in the nomenclature and taxonomy of the disease-producing fungi and at the same time to present clearly the clinical and pathological aspects of the subject.

The book is recommended with confidence to veterinarians and to all who have an interest in diseases of animals associated with fungi.

A. W. STABLEFORTH

Weybridge,
7th November 1958.

PREFACE

The revival of interest in medical mycology during recent years has stimulated a re-assessment of the importance of the mycoses of animals. Current knowledge of the mycoses of man has been codified in the well-known American Manual of clinical mycology by Conant, Smith, Baker, Callaway & Martin (1954), but the mycoses of animals have never been comprehensively reviewed. Much of the early work in this field is unreliable and much more information on diverse aspects of mycotic infections of animals, and particularly on pathology, is required before a standard work of reference can be compiled. This review is largely an attempt to survey all aspects of the literature of fungal infections of higher animals as conveniently as possible for anyone having an interest in these infections whether as veterinarian, mycologist or medical man.

Beginning as a bibliography compiled during a survey undertaken during 1952–54 of the fungi found associated with disease in farm and domestic animals in Great Britain, references to conditions not found in this country were subsequently added. The final result shows a certain unevenness due in part to deficiencies in the literature and in part to the special interests of the authors. As far as possible the originals of the publications cited have been scanned if not read. Many of the references checked, especially those compiled in later publications, have been omitted from the bibliography but it is hoped that sufficient numbers have been retained to establish the sources of the information and opinions on any topic and to give an interested enquirer clues to any further information available. In general, the literature is covered to the end of 1957.

The illustrations have been selected from a large collection and many are original. We are indebted to J. T. Done (Fig. 21); M. Labitte (Fig. 17); J. S. Paterson (Fig. 10); H. T. Davies (Fig. 9); R. G. Menges (Fig. 12); and to E. Clements for much photographic assistance.

This review was begun at the University of Exeter under the auspices of the Agricultural Research Council to which we tender our thanks, and we are greatly indebted to the staff of the Commonwealth Bureau of Animal Health for their continued help. We are particularly grateful to the former Director of the Bureau Mr. W.A. Pool and to his successor Mr.M.Crawford for their encouragement and guidance. The following librarians have greatly assisted us in obtaining many publications: Mr. A. Gray, Central Veterinary Laboratory, Weybridge; Miss M. M. Raymer, Royal College of Veterinary Surgeons; Mr. L. J. Lloyd, University of Exeter.

G. C. A.
P. K. C. A.

CONTENTS

LIST OF BLACK AND WHITE PLATES

LIST OF COLOUR PLATES

Chapter 1

ASPERGILLOSIS
(Aspergillus fumigatus and other species)

Aspergillosis is a primary respiratory and occasionally generalized infection caused by species of Aspergillus. It is world-wide in distribution and has been recorded in almost all domestic animals and birds as well as many wild species. The disease is characterized by the formation of yellowish caseous nodules or plaques and has been known to affect almost every organ of the body. Diagnosis is by the demonstration of hyphae in the lesions and by the culture of the pathogen. Iodide therapy has been used with some success in human infections, but few animal cases have been diagnosed before death. The removal of the source of the fungus spores appears to be the only satisfactory method of control.

Aspergillosis has been recorded in almost every species of domesticated animal and bird and in a great many free-living and captive wild creatures. It was one of the first of the mycoses of animals to be described and helped to focus attention on the microbial causes of disease at a time when bacteria were still microscopical curiosities. From the time of its discovery in a jay by Mayer & Emmert in 1815, until the end of the nineteenth century a great many papers appeared on the disease, including a number of monographic treatments, and as a result, much of our present knowledge of the disease was already known by 1900. Relatively few reports have appeared since that time, but within the past few years renewed interest has led to the confirmation of much of the earlier work and has provided a better understanding of the role of Aspergillus fumigatus and other fungi in respiratory diseases in both man and animals. There is no recent general review of aspergillosis and the outstanding works of Rénon (1897) and Lucet (1897) have remained the standard texts for sixty years.

AVIAN ASPERGILLOSIS

Disease Name. Aspergillosis. Syn. Pneumonomycosis, Bronchomycosis, Cytomycosis, Brooder pneumonia, and in part Pseudotuberculosis and Mycosis; in ostriches Chick fever and Yellow liver. Pneumonie du couveuse (Fr.).

Pathogens. Aspergillus fumigatus Fresenius, 1850–53. Syn. A. nigrescens Robin, 1853; A. aviarius Peck, 1891.
Aspergillus flavus Link, 1809. (Schieblich, 1921).
Aspergillus niger van Tieghem, 1867. (Hare, 1937).
Aspergillus nidulans (Eidam) Wint., 1884. (Ainsworth & Rewell, 1949).
Aspergillus terreus Thom, 1916. (Ainsworth & Austwick, 1955a).

Hosts. Domesticated and caged birds; fowl, turkey, duck, goose, pigeon, canary, budgerigar, parrot, ostrich. Captive wild birds, especially water birds; duck, geese, penguin, stork, flamingo, cormorant, parrot, hawk, owl, pheasant, peafowl. Free-living wild birds; wood-pigeon, seagull, rook, pheasant, sparrow, swan, jay, grouse, Manx shearwater, thrush.

Geographical Distribution.
World-wide. Severe economic losses occur, chiefly in areas of intensive rearing.

The striking post-mortem picture presented by avian aspergillosis was no doubt responsible for its early recognition so that by the end of the nineteenth century some 60 contributions had been made on the disease of birds alone. At first there was little attempt to identify the "green mould" seen in the air-sac and bronchial lesions (Owen, 1832) and many of the early accounts are difficult to interpret for this reason. There was also much confusion between the pathogenic and saprophytic species of Aspergillus. Progress in the study of the disease was also slowed by controversy over the aetiological significance of the fungi found sporulating on the lesions and although the primary pathogenicity of most of these is now well established, the epidemiology and development of the disease still require further investigation.

There are extensive reviews of avian aspergillosis by Lesbouyries (1941), Urbain & Guillot (1938) and Verge (1927), in which may be found detailed accounts of the species of birds affected, and of the pathology, diagnosis, mycology and therapy of the disease.

Symptomatology. Because almost any organ of the avian body may be affected by aspergillosis, the symptoms are extremely varied. They may be respiratory, digestive or nervous and occur in birds of all ages.

Acute aspergillosis — This typically occurs in very young birds and may be associated with considerable losses. Watkins (1940), for instance, estimated that 10% of all deaths in chicks under 14 days old were caused by this disease. Typically there is loss of appetite, increased respiration, a rise in temperature, listlessness, foetid diarrhoea and rapid loss of condition. Convulsions sometimes occur and affected birds often die within 24—48 hours of the onset of symptoms. Epidemic outbreaks in young birds frequently have a very high death rate before control measures can be taken. Similar symptoms may occur in pullorum disease (Salmonella pullorum), from which this form of aspergillosis must be distinguished.

Chronic aspergillosis — The onset of this form is insidious and the affected birds may survive for long periods in a gradually declining state. The symptoms of the acute disease are often present in a milder form together with anaemia, yellowing of the faeces and the presence of a respiratory rattle. The chronic disease generally occurs sporadically and is the usual form in adult birds.

Pathology. Although the appearance of the lesions is almost diagnostic, it is necessary to eliminate tuberculosis and other granulomatous diseases. Differential diagnosis can be conclusive if the fungus is fruiting within the respiratory cavities of the bird but as this only occurs in the chronic stages of the disease, the demonstration of hyphae in the nodules is the most useful method. This is carried out by crushing the whole or a piece of a nodule under a coverslip on a slide in a drop of 20% potassium hydroxide or in lactophenol cotton blue. The hyphae can usually be seen projecting from the edges of the masses of caseous material and if the latter technique is used they will stain deeply.

Lungs – In the lungs the acute form typically appears as yellowish-white miliary nodules 1–3 mm. in diameter which are generally evenly distributed throughout the tissue. Each nodule is surrounded by a dark infiltrated zone, the remainder of the lung appearing normal. Chronic lesions either result from the coalescence of many nodules or are formed by the enlargement of single ones and may eventually become calcified. A peracute pneumonic form also occurs in which there is complete congestion of lung tissue without the formation of nodules.

Air-sacs – The serous membrane of the air-sacs becomes thickened in places by the development of small yellowish-white plaque-like lesions which enlarge rapidly, become raised in the centre, and then coalesce to form a complete membranous or caseous lining to the serosa up to 5 mm. thick.

Bronchi and Trachea – These organs may become blocked either by lesions similar to those described in the air-sacs, or, in the pneumonic form, by mucoid discharge.
Wherever the surface of a lesion is exposed to the air, the conidiophores of A. fumigatus can develop, forming the characteristic greenish-blue or dark grey patches of sporing heads so often described by early observers.

Lesions in sites other than the respiratory organs are generally chronic:-

Alimentary canal – Plaque-like lesions may occur in the mouth, the gizzard and the intestines especially in turkeys (Lignières & Petit, 1898).

Liver, spleen, kidneys and ovaries – Nodular lesions have been found in all these organs sometimes associated with those in adjacent abdominal air-sacs (Emmel, 1929). Peritonitis is not uncommon and the disease in ostrich chicks has been termed "yellow liver" (Walker, 1915).

Nervous system – The occurrence of nervous symptoms in aspergillosis including convulsions and torticollis has been partly attributed by Henrici (1939) to the production of toxins by the growth of A. fumigatus in the body. There are however several reports of abscesses in the cerebrum and cerebellum containing the hyphae of A. fumigatus both in the presence (Raines et al., 1956) and absence (Jungherr & Gifford, 1944) of pulmonary and other lesions.

Eyes – Lesions have been noted in the eyes of baby chicks by

Hudson (1947) and in turkeys by Moore (1953), the latter author finding the condition significantly more common in males than in females.

Bones and joints — Osteo-arthritis may be set up in the joints with subsequent lameness (Bizard & Pommay, 1887) and lesions in the long bones were observed very early by Heusinger (1821).

Skin — There is some doubt as to the reliability of the reports of skin infection (Lahaye, 1928), mostly because of the inability of the aspergilli to utilize keratin. Moulds can always be isolated from the skin of birds, where they are probably present as spores, and any sustained moist condition of the skin will lead to their germination.

Following castration — Babić (1930) reported infection with Aspergillus fumigatus at the site of surgical caponization, with spread to the liver and the air-sacs, and a similar incident was reported by Chute et al. (1955).

In the nodular lesions, there is a central necrotic zone containing a radiating mass of branching hyphae (2–3 micra diam.). These hyphae are generally clearly septate but may be either irregular in outline and appear to consist of swollen segments, or of normal elongated appearance and very sparsely septate. Numerous epithelioid and giant cells surround this centre and outside is a reaction zone of eosinophiles, lymphocytes and fibrous tissue (Lesbouyries, 1941). Völker (1924) claimed that the presence of eosinophiles was in itself sufficient to distinguish the infection from tuberculosis, which however may also be present in the same bird (Ainsworth & Rewell, 1949).

The development of the lesions has been followed in detail only by Nicolaus (1934). He found that lesions produced experimentally in the air-sacs of fowls were visible within eight hours of inoculation by the intratracheal route. At twelve hours they consisted of subepithelial nodules formed from pseudo-eosinophiles accumulating around the invading fungus hyphae. At three days he observed the temporary development of conidiophores within the central necrotic zone, the formation of daughter nodules and the appearance of histiocytes, epithelioid cells and giant cells. In the later stages a many-layered fibrous capsule was formed round the necrotic centre and the lesions reached a diameter of 25 mm. in twenty-two days.

Mycology. Diagnosis by direct examination of the lesions is not always successful and the isolation of the pathogen must always be undertaken to identify the species. The best method is to plate out small pieces of the lesions or affected tissues on to malt agar or Sabouraud glucose agar, containing antibacterial antibiotics. Mycelial growth is usually visible within twenty-four hours at 37°C. and the characteristic conidiophores are often produced within two days.

Aspergillus fumigatus is the commonest cause of avian aspergillosis. It was first described by Fresenius in 1850–53 from the lungs of a great bustard in the Frankfurt zoo but many of the earlier records of avian aspergillosis would appear to have been associated with this species

PLATE I

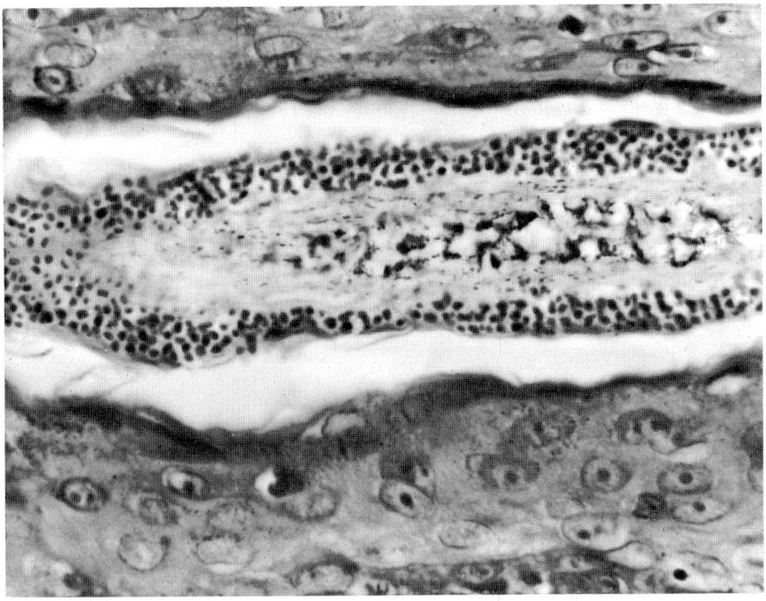

FIG. 1 Dog Ringworm. Section of hair showing spore sheath of *Microsporum canis*. Stained periodic acid-Schiff. ×500.

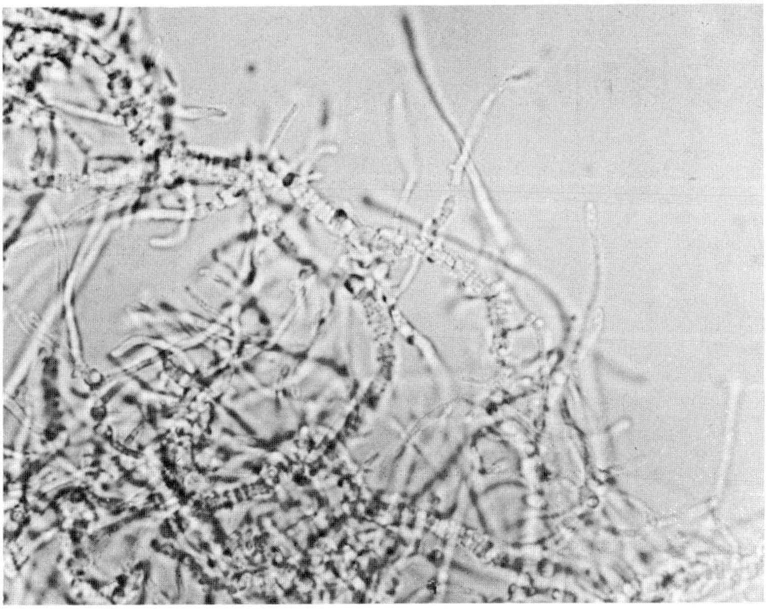

FIG. 2. Mycotic dermatitis. *Dermatophilus dermatonomus* filaments in three day culture in serum broth. ×500.

PLATE II

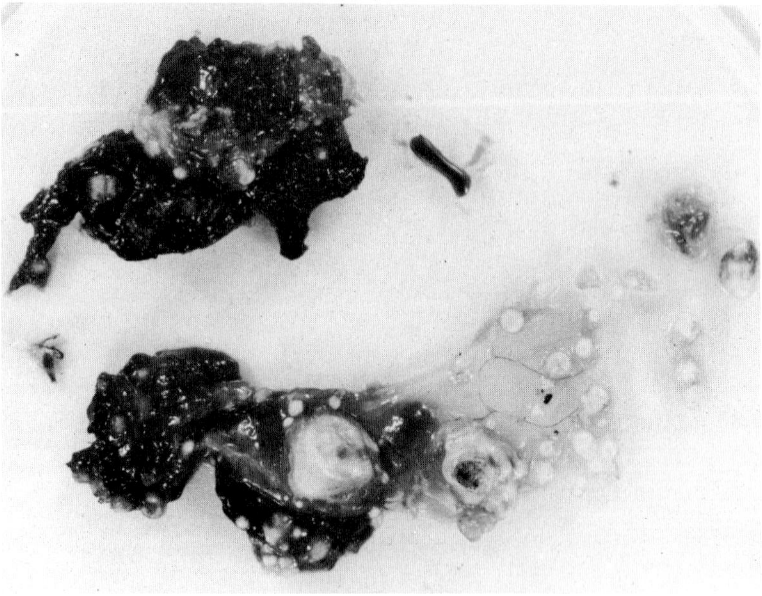

FIG. 3. Aspergillosis. Plaque-like lesions of *Aspergillus fumigatus* infection on air-sac membrane of Abyssinian blue-winged goose.

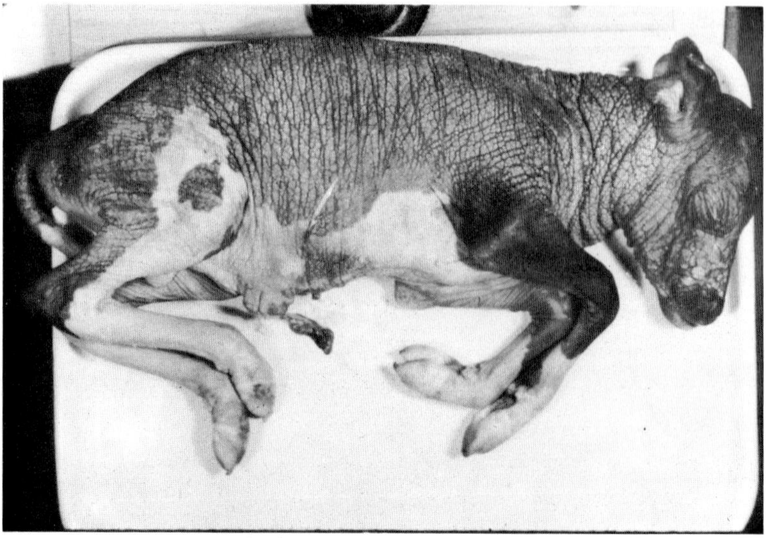

FIG. 4. Mycotic abortion. Bovine foetus aborted at 7 months showing skin lesions associated with *Aspergillus fumigatus*.

PLATE III

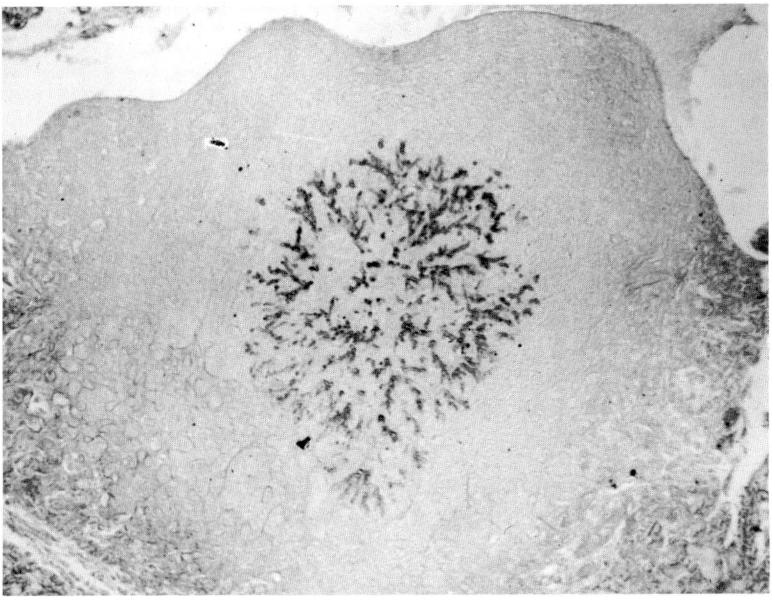

FIG. 5. Aspergillosis. Section of lung lesion in penguin, showing radiating hyphae of *Aspergillus fumigatus*. Stained periodic acid-Schiff. ×170.

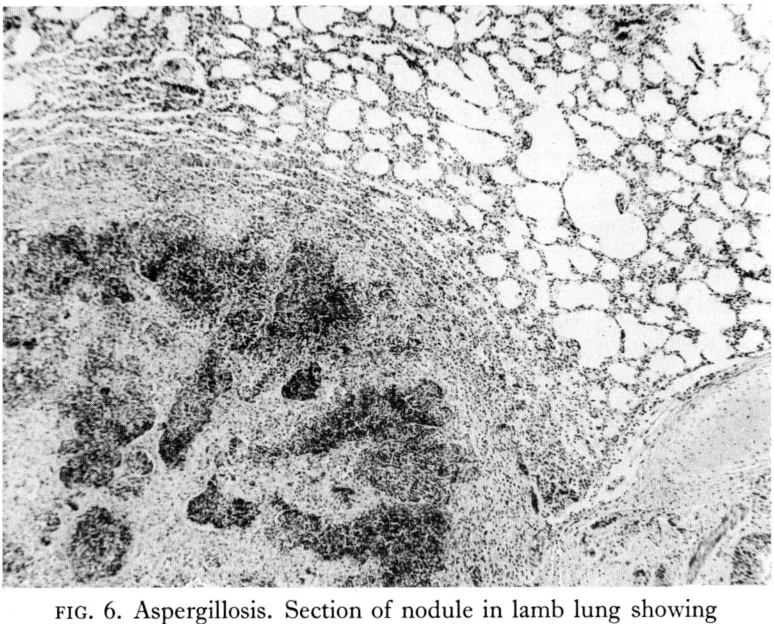

FIG. 6. Aspergillosis. Section of nodule in lamb lung showing granulomatous foci and compression of alveoli (*Aspergillus fumigatus*). Stained haematoxylin and eosin. ×50.

PLATE IV

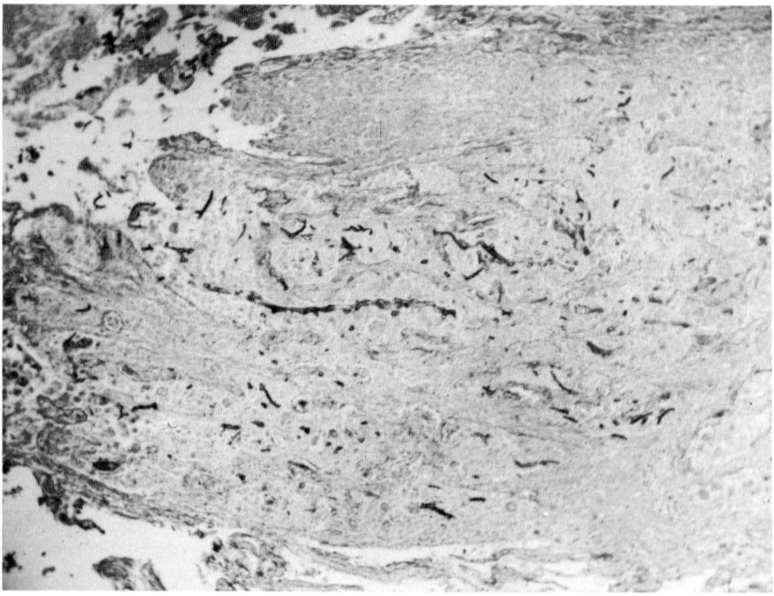

FIG. 7. Mycotic abortion. Section of maternal caruncle showing invasion by hyphae of *Absidia ramosa*. Stained periodic acid-Schiff. ×150.

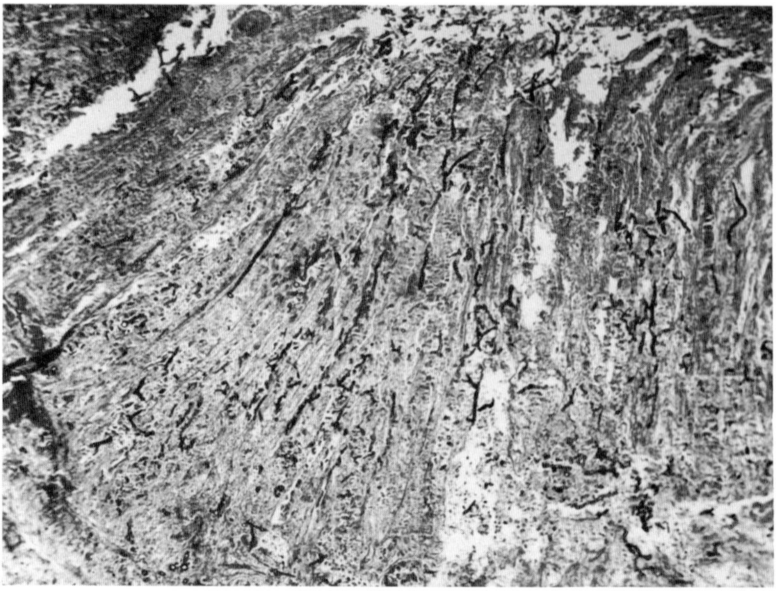

FIG. 8. Mucormycotic ulceration. Wall of abomasum of calf, showing invasion by a mucoraceous fungus. Stained periodic acid-Schiff. ×150.

although the descriptions are inadequate for certain identification. Other species of Aspergillus have also been incriminated (see list of pathogens) of which A. flavus and A. nidulans are probably the most frequent (Schieblich, 1921; Ainsworth & Rewell, 1949). Yet further species reported from birds include A. glaucus (Spring, 1848), A. candidus (Rayer & Montagne, 1842) and A. dubius (Heusinger, 1821) but these are either well known saprophytes which were undoubtedly contaminants (e.g. A. glaucus series) or were doubtful identifications of pathogenic species.

The identification of the different species of Aspergillus has been greatly facilitated by the manual of Thom & Raper (1945) and this can be referred to for keys and descriptions. The genus Aspergillus is characterized by the formation of a vesicle on the end of the upright conidiophore, followed by the appearance of peg-like structures over its surface. These are the sterigmata and they form chains of conidia from their distal ends, giving the columns of spores seen in culture. The different species are primarily distinguished on the structure of the sporing "heads" and on the colour of the spore mass. A few Aspergillus spp. form the "perfect" state in culture and are classed as Ascomycetes. In these, e.g. A. nidulans, the asci are formed inside closed fruiting bodies called cleistothecia and each contains up to eight ascospores. This type of spore probably plays little part in the epidemiology of aspergillosis although ascospores are generally more resistant to adverse conditions than conidia.

There is some evidence that moulds other than Aspergillus spp. can cause similar lesions, but a great many of such reports appear to be due to the high rate of contamination of bird lungs by the spores of saprophytic fungi (Baker et al., 1934). Proof of infection by these fungi must depend on the isolation of a species with the same hyphal morphology as that seen in the lesions. Further work should show whether different species of Aspergillus cause distinct forms of the disease as for example in the association of caseating pneumonia with A. niger reported by Hare (1937).

Strain variation and Susceptibility. Although Henrici (1939) states that "many strains of A. fumigatus isolated from air or vegetation show no pathogenicity" there seems little confirmation of this and a remarkable constancy in morphology and pathogenicity is a characteristic of this species. Occasional isolates are white, floccose and produce few spores, but these have not been reported from birds.

On the other hand considerable variation occurs in the susceptibility of different varieties of domestic birds to aspergillosis. Generali (1879) first showed that the finer bred races of pigeon succumbed to the disease more readily than others, and Asthana (1944) considered that the races of Rhode Island Red hens he studied were affected more seriously than Black Minorcas or White Leghorns. Brooksbank & Austwick (1955) showed how heavy losses in a hatchery occurred only in the weeks when eggs from inbreeding pens were hatching, whilst the alternating crossbred hatches escaped infection although in the same incubator. This outbreak also suggested that certain strains of Rhode Island Reds and White Leghorns were apparently more susceptible than others.

Epidemiology. There is no doubt that infection follows the inhalation of fungus spores from mouldy litter, grain, meal or other sources. The quantitative aspects of natural infection are quite unknown but the main habitat of *A. fumigatus* and other pathogenic species is in rotting plant and animal material especially damp hay, straw and grain which have heated up during storage. In this way *A. fumigatus* may become the predominant mould.

Although the source of infection for domestic fowls may often be traceable it is not so with aspergillosis in free-living and captive wild birds. Davis & McClung (1940) said that *A. fumigatus* developing in rotting seaweed was responsible for widespread deaths in herring gulls at Boston, U.S.A., whilst mouldy combine straw has been considered to have led to the deaths of pheasants. In captive water birds the litter and food are generally regarded as the inoculum source, but Ainsworth & Rewell (1949) found advanced cases in birds which had been captured only two days previously so that infection must have been present in the wild.

In connexion with the occurrence of aspergillosis in wild geese, Sladen & Austwick (1955) undertook a study of the fungus flora of the upper respiratory tracts of wild pink footed geese in Iceland and Scotland. They were unable to detect the presence of *A. fumigatus* in throat swabs from these birds but found over a dozen other species of fungi which were thought to have been present as spores. The source of infection for free-living wild birds is still obscure.

Treatment and Control. The treatment of avian aspergillosis is influenced by the lack of clinical diagnosis, for the symptoms are not specific and generally the peak of mortality has been passed before any therapeutic measures can be instituted. Because of this reports of successful treatment or even spontaneous recovery are doubtful.

Various methods have been used in the direct treatment of individual birds. They include the inhalation of tar vapours (Otte, 1928), chlorine or sulphur dust, but so far no information is available concerning the use of iodide therapy which has been successfully employed in the experimental disease in rabbits and also in human cases.

By far the most effective method of control is by removing the source of infection, *i.e.*, the mouldy litter or food; this should be burned and the premises adequately cleaned out, perhaps using a fungicidal solution. Another method of prevention is described by Urbain & Guillot (1938), who regularly fed the penguins in the Paris zoo with 5–6 mg. of potassium iodide daily for eight consecutive days in each month, each dose being inserted into a fish. By this technique they found that the incidence of aspergillosis in these birds was greatly reduced. Good sanitation and careful control of feedingstuffs and litter remain the best methods of prevention in domestic birds.

Egg Infection. *Aspergillus fumigatus* can readily attack both fresh and incubating eggs once it has gained entry through the shell. Infection does not seem to occur in the oviduct but results from the external contamination of the shell after laying. Penetration occurs through the pores of the shell and the fungus grows well on the shell membranes, killing the embryo if present and occasionally penetrating into the white. Eventually conidiophores and spores are formed in the air-space and affected eggs can be detected by candling. On breaking open the air-space the greenish felt of hyphae and spores is seen.

The chief fungus reported from eggs in incubation is A. fumigatus but several others have been obtained from stored eggs. Of these probably Cladosporium herbarum is the most important in causing the "black spot" discoloration reported by Weston & Halnan (1927). Lucet (1897) demonstrated that clean eggs cannot be infected by direct application of the spores of A. fumigatus and that it was necessary to put a thin layer of butter or other grease on the shell before infection would take place. Hence he concluded that dirty eggs were more liable to infection than clean, and cited an outbreak of egg infection in ducks in which the nests were heavily contaminated with A. fumigatus.

MAMMALIAN ASPERGILLOSIS

Disease Name. Aspergillosis. Syn. pneumonomycosis aspergillina, bronchomycosis.

Pathogen. Aspergillus fumigatus Fresenius (Zürn, 1876).
Aspergillus nidulans (Eidam) Wint. (Tscherniak, 1928).
Aspergillus flavus Link (Tscherniak, 1928).

Hosts. Cattle (Zürn, 1876), horse (Rivolta, 1856), sheep (Mazzanti, 1884), pig (Berg, 1898–99), cat (Sautter et al., 1955), dog (Gotti, 1871), guinea-pig (Ainsworth & Austwick, 1955a), rabbit (Smit, 1915), bison (Rewell & Ainsworth, 1947), hare (Thjøtta, 1933), deer (Rousseau & Serrurier, 1841), goat (Mori, 1916), monkey (Scott, 1928).

Geographical Distribution.
Europe, North America, South-East Asia and New Zealand.

Except in man, aspergillosis is not a well-known disease of mammals, although it has been recognized with increasing frequency in the past few years and the literature now consists of approximately a hundred papers dating from the brief mention of the disease in a deer by Rousseau & Serrurier (1841). It is probable that the most important aspect of mammalian aspergillosis is in connexion with mycotic abortion (see p. 53), in which infection of the placenta of cows is thought to be a sequel to subclinical pulmonary aspergillosis. The aspergilli may also contribute to allergic types of respiratory troubles such as pneumonitis and asthma, especially in young animals. There is no recent review of mammalian aspergillosis, but Rénon (1897) gave a comprehensive survey of the cases up to that time.

Symptomatology. Most of the reported cases have been of the pulmonary disease, but generalization has been described. The clinical condition greatly resembles tuberculosis and is characterized by general wasting, followed by death.

As in avian aspergillosis a large number of the accounts are unsatisfactory both from the clinical and the mycological points of view. A few are no more than passing references to cases in which the fungus concerned has not always even been classed as an *Aspergillus* sp., and because of this the published reports have been carefully examined before their inclusion as apparently authentic cases.

The different forms of the disease in animals have not been studied sufficiently for a workable classification to be given, but the categories made by Rénon (1897) of chronic, acute and subacute may still be used. When a large enough number of cases is on record it should be possible to distinguish the different clinical manifestations of aspergillosis with reference to the type of lesion and its stage of development, individual susceptibility, and the allergic and environmental factors of each case.

Cattle. Although there are several earlier reports of aspergillosis in bovines, that of Bournay (1895) in an eight-year-old cow is one of the better documented accounts. The symptoms developed in fifteen days in this case from a slight cough to laboured respiration, bloody and foetid diarrhoea, slight fever and loss of appetite. The pulmonary lesions consisted of cavitated sub-pleural nodules and interlobular emphysema, whilst there was inflammation of the small intestine. Typical pulmonary infection with nodule formation was also reported by Pearson & Ravenel (1900) and further reports have been made at intervals (Bartolucci, 1903; Del Giudice, 1956). Bendixen (1926) described what appeared to have been a case of generalized aspergillosis in a cow with invasion of the lungs, liver, spleen and kidneys, and another form of the disease was reported by Lucet (1897) in which generalized interstitial haemorrhage was a pronounced feature and the lungs showed centres of hepatization without nodule formation.

Horse. Aspergillosis in horses was recorded earlier than in cattle (Rivolta, 1856) but was frequently restricted to infection of the nasal sinuses and the guttural pouches (Ries, 1903). Foulerton (1899) described the lung of a horse with typical aspergillotic nodules and Nöller & Krause (1924) and Tscherniak (1928) gave details of several more cases. Meningeal involvement was reported by Romanov (1928). In the case described by Thary & Lucet (1895) in a four-year-old mare the disease developed rapidly and showed generalized interstitial haemorrhage with caseous nodules in the kidneys.

Sheep. There have been only five reports of aspergillosis in sheep. The lesions in lambs consist of small (2–3 mm. diam.) bluish-grey nodules surrounded by a narrow haemorrhagic zone, and closely resemble those caused by the lungworm *Muellerius capillaris* (Andersen, 1927). The most recent report of the disease is in the Annual Report of the New Zealand Department of Agriculture for 1955.

Van Hellens (1902–03) investigated in Finland one of the few epidemics of aspergillosis on record among sheep. The animals were adult and showed chronic bronchitis and catarrhal pneumonia closely resembling the symptoms of tuberculosis. Death occurred up to one year after the appearance of symptoms. Conidiophores of *A. fumigatus* were found in the sputum of affected sheep and numerous discrete and sometimes well calcified nodules 1–7 mm. in diam. were present in the lungs. Nobel & Shamir (1956) described a rather different condition in which granulomatous lesions containing the hyphae of *A. fumigatus* were found in the lungs of a day-old lamb, and they considered the infection had taken place *in utero*.

Pig. Records of aspergillosis in pigs are also rare. Berg (1898–99) first described the disease as a persistent cough associated with a lobar pneumonia and nodule formation. The spleen and kidney were enlarged and congested, and nodular lesions were found in the mesenteric lymph nodes. Berg did not obtain any isolates from the lesions but assumed that an *Aspergillus* was the cause of the disease. Generalized infection in a pig was also reported by Nuvoletti & Casella (1903).

Other species of domestic animals. Spontaneous aspergillosis in domestic rabbits has been reported by Schöppler (1919) and Höppli (1923), whilst Ainsworth & Austwick (1955a) have recorded the disease in guinea-pigs. Apparently no authentic case of pulmonary aspergillosis has been found in the dog for the main records from this animal by Gotti (1871) and Stazzi (1905) are of nasal and auricular fungal infection due to a variety of fungi. A case in a cat has been described by Sautter *et al.* (1955) and Ainsworth & Austwick (1955a) briefly report the occurrence of a large aspergillotic nodule in the udder of a goat which was associated with chronic mastitis.

Wild animals. As in birds, captive wild mammals have provided several examples of aspergillosis. Dobberstein (1936) reported a case of meningeal infection in an elk in the Berlin zoo, whilst Rewell & Ainsworth (1947) showed how the respiratory passages of an American bison at the London zoo were found on *post-mortem* examination to be lined with a greenish felt of *A. fumigatus* in the absence of severe lung lesions.

Scott (1930) gave details of nine cases of mycosis (aspergillosis?) and a further nine associated with tuberculosis in captive monkeys encountered at the London zoo. The lungs were the chief organs involved but miliary nodules were occasionally found throughout the viscera.

Free-living wild animals have also been found infected by *A. fumigatus* and outbreaks of pulmonary aspergillosis have been reported in hares in Sweden (Thjøtta, 1933; Hülphers & Lilleengen, 1947) and also in roe-deer in that country and Switzerland, in which the conchal and ethmoid bones as well as the lungs and other organs became affected by tumour-like growths containing hyphae (Krembs, 1937; Burgisser, 1955). When specific determination had been carried out, *A. fumigatus* was the most frequent isolate but Burgeon (1929) reported *A. niger* from nodular lesions in the lungs of a bull, a heifer and a stag in Indo-China.

Pathology. The diagnosis of aspergillosis in mammals may be made, as in birds, by crushing the nodules for microscopic examination and by isolation. Even in the pneumonic form of the disease, hyphae can generally be seen in the lung tissue without difficulty and in the soft nodules from lamb lungs they have been found in great profusion (Watkins & Austwick, unpublished data). It may also be possible to examine the sputum and nasal discharge of large animals, bearing in mind however that this material reflects the atmospheric spore content of the environment and the results require careful interpretation.

Many of the pathological features of avian aspergillosis have been found in mammals, but chronic lesions seem to be more frequent probably because of the relatively longer life of the latter. The lung nodules generally have a central necrotic zone containing hyphae, surrounded by atelectiased pulmonary tissue. At a later stage cavitation may occur with the development of an internal greenish, powdery surface consisting of the sporing heads of Aspergillus fumigatus (Bournay, 1895). Bendixen (1926) described the pathology of the nodular lesions in the liver, kidney and spleen of a cow as showing severe interstitial infiltration. Unfortunately no isolate was obtained from this case but the morphology of the hyphae in the lesions corresponded to infection by an Aspergillus sp. The development of the nodules in the lungs of sheep was traced by Van Hellens (1902–03) from small accumulations of leucocytes and red blood corpuscles in the blood vessels to calcified lesions in which a few giant cells were present together with extensive invasion by fibroblasts.

Occasionally in chronic infections closely radiating groups of hyphae are found in the kidneys or spleen and these have been termed the "actinomycotic forms" of A. fumigatus. Lichtheim (1882) first observed them and Nicaud (1928) produced them experimentally by repeated inoculation of spores into rabbits. Drake (1948) also saw these forms in long-standing experimental infections with A. nidulans. They were considered by Renon (1897) to indicate the extreme defence of the organs of the body and a lowered vitality of the fungus. Other structures sometimes encountered are the "asteroid" bodies surrounding hyphae which consist of radiating acidophilic processes, closely resembling the "clubs" seen in actinomycotic granules.

Epidemiology. Mammalian aspergillosis is most probably a primary pulmonary disease which is non-contagious and is contracted by exposure to large numbers of fungal spores from mouldy hay, etc. The presence of the viable spores of A. fumigatus and many other fungi in hay is easily demonstrated by culture, and mouldy samples appear to support a tremendous fungal growth. The events which follow the inhalation of spores are still largely unknown but Lucet (1897) claimed to have detected spores in the blood stream, which was a means of dissemination also considered by Følger (1906–07). The latter went further however in suggesting that the interstitial nature of the lung lesions in the cow he examined indicated that infection was of embolic origin and had spread from the inflamed uterus by thrombosis of the uterine veins.

It seems that housed animals fed on hay during the winter are more likely to inhale large numbers of fungus spores and it will be surprising if many more cases of aspergillosis are not diagnosed following the development of methods for the detection of subclinical infection. Tscherniak (1928) has claimed that the routine examination of horses for glanders revealed an incidence of aspergillosis of 16%, whilst earlier (1924) he had given details of seventy-eight cases of the disease in horses. The incidence of aspergillosis in cattle has yet to be estimated, even though it may be of considerable importance in relation to mycotic abortion. Figures are not available for other animals.

Prognosis and Treatment. As in birds, aspergillosis has rarely been diagnosed in a live animal and in consequence there are few accounts of successful treatment. Moreover the prognosis is grave since Van Hellens (1902–03) found that only a very few sheep out of a flock of eighty survived the slow infection.

Control would appear to be best carried out by the methods described under the avian disease, i.e., by the careful removal of the source of infection. Rénon (1897) found that potassium iodide given intravenously increased the survival time of rabbits inoculated with spores of *Aspergillus fumigatus* and the method has frequently been used in the therapy of the human disease (Conant *et al.*, 1954, p. 71).

Serology and Toxicology. The serological study of aspergillosis is unfortunately not nearly so advanced as in histoplasmosis and coccidioidomycosis. Reliable serological diagnostic methods would be particularly useful in large animals in which radiography is difficult, and in which subclinical infection appears to be more common than at present supposed.

Complement-fixation was found by Bøe *et al.* (1939) to be the most sensitive method for the detection of antibodies. They obtained titres of 1:1000 to 1:1600 irrespective of whether spores or the powdered mycelium was used as the antigen. The agglutination and precipitin tests performed were as unsuccessful as those performed by Macaigne & Nicaud (1927a). Matsumoto (1929) obtained a titre of 1:10 for *A. fumigatus* and an inhibition of haemolysis by *A. amstelodami* of 1:320. Tests for skin sensitivity have been successfully used in man by Macaigne & Nicaud (1927b), Hyde *et al.* (1956) and others, but urgently require further study.

Research on production of toxins has mostly been carried out using *A. fumigatus* but often with conflicting results. Leber (1882), Ceni & Besta (1905) and Bodin & Lenormand (1912) all considered that they had evidence of toxin production, but this was contrary to the findings of Kotliar (1894) and Obici (1898). Henrici (1939) seems to have clearly demonstrated the presence of an endotoxin in *A. fumigatus* and Salvin (1952) later confirmed this observation. Henrici found that a thermolabile substance could be extracted by cutting up, squeezing and centrifuging the mycelium, and that this affected all experimental animals when injected by subcutaneous, intraperitoneal and intravenous routes, producing nervous symptoms and proving fatal in quite small doses. Many of the properties of the toxin indicated that it was a toxalbumin but it was apparently a non-protein substance.

Immunity. There is no record of immunity to aspergillosis in animals following recovery from the disease, chiefly because so few cases have been diagnosed before death. Of the experimental attempts to produce immunity, those recorded by Rénon (1897) appear to have been the most extensive. Using over fifty animals he found that only three rabbits showed any signs of resistance to infection after progressively greater doses of spores. Other attempts at immunization, using antisera, killed spores and attenuated strains of A. fumigatus, were unsuccessful. Henrici (1939) was able to produce immunity to aspergillosis in rabbits using the endotoxin he obtained from the mycelium and found that this immunity could be transferred passively to guinea-pigs and mice.

Experimental aspergillosis. The earliest experimental inoculations were made in Germany by Grohe (1870) and Bloch (1870) both of whom claimed to have produced nodular lesions in rabbits with A. glaucus and Penicillium glaucum. Grawitz repeated this work without success in 1877 but succeeded in 1881. Various attempts were made to explain this but Lichtheim (1882) effectively demonstrated that these workers had been using impure cultures which grew the pathogenic Aspergillus fumigatus at high temperature of incubation and the non-pathogenic A. glaucus (which may superficially resemble it) at a lower temperature. The two species are easily distinguished by the much smaller size of the spores of the former.

Most of the later experimental work has been concentrated on A. fumigatus and a great range of experimental animals has been found susceptible. In birds, the pigeon is the most easily infected, but intra-tracheal inoculation is generally successful in most domestic species. Rabbits and guinea-pigs are highly susceptible by the intravenous route but cats, dogs and sheep are said to be refractory (Rénon, 1897; Lucet, 1897).

The route of inoculation influences the ultimate development of the disease, intravenous inoculation in rabbits characteristically giving rise to renal lesions and subcutaneous inoculation to small abscesses. Intestinal infection has been produced in rabbits by feeding excessive quantities of spores (Rénon, 1897) and arthritis can be caused by injection of spores into the joints. Inoculation of the cornea causes a keratitis which may lead to the invasion of the eye and in calves, Bendixen (1928) observed infection of the eye in one animal and extensive pneumonia in another inoculated by this route. This author's experimental production of abortion in cattle with A. fumigatus is described in the section on mycotic abortion.

Apparently the size of the inoculum is critical, at least by the intra-venous route. Rénon (1897) found a direct relationship between the quantity of spores injected and the survival of the animal. The earliest time of death with large numbers of spores was 4–7 days. Henrici (1939) found that large intravenous doses in pigeons caused haemorrhagic necrosis with little reaction, whilst very small doses gave a typical picture of miliary nodules after a longer time. On the other hand whilst the blowing of large numbers of spores into the trachea caused rapidly fatal pneumonia, the feeding of heavily infected grain produced the chronic form of the disease. The quantitative relations of spores to infection appear to be the key to the epidemiology and pathology of aspergillosis.

Chapter 2

MONILIASIS
(Species of Candida)

Moniliasis is a general term covering diseases caused by mycelial yeasts of the genus Candida, especially by C. albicans. Infection is usually restricted to the alimentary canal, but generalization may occur. Among animals, moniliasis of poultry (especially turkeys) is of particular importance. C. albicans, though at times undoubtedly a primary pathogen, is frequently found in association with apparently normal animals.

Disease Name. Moniliasis (syn. Thrush, Candidiasis). Mouget (Fr.); Soor (Ger.)

Pathogen. Candida albicans (Robin) Berkhout, 1923. Syn. Oidium albicans Robin, 1853; Monilia albicans (Robin) Zopf, 1890; Mycotorula albicans (Robin) Langeron & Talice, 1932; see Lodder & Van Rij (1952), p. 466 for many more.

Hosts. Birds (fowls, turkeys, ducks, geese, guinea-fowl, pigeons), cattle, pig, dog, hedgehog, guinea-pig, various rodents, monkey.
Also man, see Conant et al. (1954), pp. 169-195.

Geographical Distribution. World-wide.

Oral moniliasis in infants (or thrush) caused by Candida albicans has been well known for more than a century. The thrush fungus and other species of Candida have also been frequently recorded both from the lungs, skin, nails, vagina, etc. in man and there is a vast and very confused literature. Much of the confusion has been due to claims for a pathogenic association on inadequate evidence and perhaps even more to inadequate data on the fungi. No clarification is possible unless the mycological approach is satisfactory and so for moniliasis, as for ringworm (see p. 80), the general pattern adopted in this survey will be varied and the mycology will be considered first.

Mycology. The term 'yeast', which is typically applied to unicellular fungi which multiply by budding (i. e. by blastospores), has no precise mycological meaning. Some yeasts have a more or less well developed pseudomycelium or mycelium, while some mycelial fungi which have a yeast-like phase are not normally classified as yeasts. Some yeasts — the sporogenous yeasts — have perfect spores (which are usually ascospores), others — the asporogenous yeasts — have not.

The identification of yeasts, which is a highly specialized branch of mycology, has been greatly facilitated by the monograph of Lodder & Van Rij (1952) and the papers of Wickerham (e. g. Wickerham, 1951). Division into families, genera and species is made on the basis of morphological and physiological characters, a full study of which is required before an unknown isolate can be named. In order of taxonomic importance it is necessary to examine the type of sporulation, the shapes of the cells, and the development of pseudomycelium on defined media, e.g. Wickerham's yeast morphology agar. Further study of the fermentation and assimilation by the isolate of six sugars (viz. glucose, maltose, sucrose, lactose, galactose, and raffinose) is then required.

The genus Candida includes imperfect (asporogenous) yeasts which exhibit pronounced pseudomycelial development in culture, multilateral budding, and usually marked assimilative and fermentative properties. C. albicans is by far the commonest species associated with clinical moniliasis.

Experimental animals. Mice and particularly rabbits are susceptible to C. albicans. Most strains of C. albicans (whether pathogenic or saprophytic) on intravenous injection into rabbits cause death in four to five days with lesions of the kidneys and other organs. Scherr has reported that the dissemination of experimental moniliasis in mice is enhanced by supplementary inoculation with living washed cells of baker's yeast (Saccharomyces cerevisiae) (Scherr, 1953a), or by keeping the experimental animals at 5° to 12° C. or 35° to 37° C. rather than 15° to 20° C. or 28° to 32° C. (Scherr, 1953b).

Distribution of Candida. Candida albicans was, as already noted, first described as the causal agent of thrush in infants. This species can, however, be isolated from many apparently normal individuals, especially from the mouths of those with dentures (see Skinner, 1947), and is presumably spread by contact and by droplet infection. Yeasts are common saprophytes and species of Candida are not infrequently recorded from the air and soil. There are, however, few records of C. albicans from such sources. di Menna (1955a) recorded C. albicans from soil in New Zealand and Van Uden et al. (1956) isolated it from plants and other substrates in Portugal.

Ainsworth & Austwick (1955b) found C. albicans and other yeasts to be associated with both normal and abnormal animals and their records suggested that these organisms were more commonly associated with the lungs and the alimentary canal than with other sites of the animal body.

The relevance of the natural distribution of C. albicans and other yeasts to the epidemiology of moniliasis is evident and it is equally clear that great caution must usually be exercised in claiming pathogenic status for C.albicans, even when found associated with a diseased condition.

AVIAN MONILIASIS
(Candida albicans)

The occurrence of avian moniliasis, which is at times of economic importance, is sporadic. The first major epidemic was reported from the U.S.A. by Gierke (1932) who recorded 8–20% mortality in young turkeys and in the following year, also in the U.S.A., Jungherr (1933) reported the loss of 10,000 chicks in a commercial hatchery. Hart (1947) recorded outbreaks among turkeys and fowls in New South Wales and more recently still Blaxland & Fincham (1950) gave a detailed account of a series of epidemic outbreaks among turkey poults in Britain. Blaxland (1951), and

Blaxland & Markson (1954) have since reported the results of their experimental studies on this condition.

In addition moniliasis has been reported in fowls from Germany (Schlegel, 1912), Sweden (Plazikowski, 1935), France (Salgues, 1937), New Zealand (Salisbury, 1949), Poland (Borkowska-Trippenbach & Szwejkowski, 1950 – also turkeys); in turkeys from Italy (Tappi, 1952–53); in geese from Germany (Schlegel, 1921); in pigeons from Uruguay (Cassamagnaghi, 1949) and Malaya (Wells, 1955); and in guinea-fowl (*Numida meleagris*) from Ceylon (McGaughey & Bandaranayake, 1953 – also chicks and ducklings).

Symptomatology. Avian moniliasis is an infection of the upper alimentary canal and particularly of the crop. Sometimes there are lesions in the mouth. The disease has no diagnostic symptoms, even when death results, and diagnosis is usually only possible *post mortem* when characteristic lesions are found in the lining of the crop. Underwood (1955) has recently used a panendoscope for the diagnosis of moniliasis in the crops of chickens and turkey poults. As described by Blaxland & Fincham (1950), these lesions are, in acute cases, greyish-white in colour, loosely adherent to the underlying mucous membrane, and rather resemble a small quantity of curdled milk. In chronic cases the crop wall is thickened and the membrane covered by a corrugated mass of piled-up yellowish-white necrotic material resembling a piece of turkish towelling. After removal of the necrotic material the underlying surface is smooth but inflamed.

Pathology. Histological examination shows the lesion to consist of a proliferation of the stratum corneum, in the deeper layers of which pseudomycelial hyphae are present. These hyphae rarely penetrate into the rete mucosum. Yeast cells and hyphae can be seen in smears of scrapings from crop lesions.

Mycology. The diagnosis is confirmed by making isolations on malt agar. *C. albicans* ferments glucose and maltose strongly, and saccharose weakly (usually acid and no gas), but not lactose. Additional evidence by which *C. albicans* can be identified is by the smooth, thick-walled, globose chlamydospores which many isolates develop readily on corn (maize) meal agar, or on the 'chlamydospore agar' described by Nickerson & Mankowski (1953).

C. albicans is usually considered to be the only pathogenic species involved. Both Jungherr (1933) and Blaxland & Fincham (1950) also found *C. krusei* associated with moniliasis but this species is usually considered to be non-pathogenic.

Epidemiology. The epidemiology of avian moniliasis still needs elucidation. It appears quite clear that during an epidemic outbreak, when healthy birds exposed to a diseased flock for 24 hours may develop a fatal infection, *C. albicans* is the primary pathogen. On the other hand, there is general agreement that it is often difficult to establish experimental infection, even by feeding massive doses of *C. albicans* derived from epidemic outbreaks, and no epidemics have yet been induced experimentally (Blaxland & Markson, 1954). Further, C. albicans can regularly be isolated from the crops of turkeys and fowls which show no clinical signs of moniliasis (from 27 to 61% of the birds according to Blaxland, 1951).

Blaxland (1951) and Blaxland & Markson (1954) have reviewed various factors which may determine the pathogenicity of C. albicans. Possibly increased virulence of the fungus plays a part. Possibly the removal of bacterial competitors of the fungus following the use of antibiotics is of importance, but there is no evidence that this is a major factor and no evidence has been offered that epidemic moniliasis is a synergic effect of a combined yeast-bacterial (or yeast-virus) infection. Alternatively, malnutrition (perhaps vitamin B deficiency) or some external factor lowers the resistance of the birds to infection.

Treatment. No satisfactory treatment is known. Hart (1947) advocated the addition of copper sulphate to the drinking water as both a control and a prophylactic measure and Salgues (1937) fed infected birds with wheat grain treated with methylene blue. Horton-Smith & Long (1952) found "Penotrane" (phenylmercuric dinaphthylmethane disulphonate) to inhibit the growth of C. albicans in vitro and suggested clinical trials with a concentration of $1:10^4$, a concentration non-toxic to chickens and turkeys.

MONILIASIS IN OTHER ANIMALS

The data regarding moniliasis in animals other than birds are scanty and frequently unsatisfactory. The following records for C. albicans may, however, be noted: from cattle (Matthias, 1941; thrush of the rumen, Germany); pigs (Kovalev, 1947; mycotic aphthous stomatitis, U.S.S.R.); Quin, 1952 (associated with death after feeding with antibiotic supplemented food, Canada); dog (Reich & Nechtow, 1949, U.S.A.); guinea-pig (Flores & Brncic, 1948; renal, Chile); hedgehog (Talice, 1932; France); rodents (Coutelen & Cochet, 1942; from faeces, associated with C. parakrusei and C. brumpti, France); monkey (Thiry, 1913; France; Catanei, 1925; Algeria). Morquer, Puget & Bazex (1953, 1954 a, b) described C. pseudotumoralis from the dog in France.

Chapter 3

CRYPTOCOCCOSIS
(Cryptococcus neoformans)

Cryptococcosis is a chronic and often fatal infection with no clear clinical pattern. In small animals the central nervous system is frequently infected. In cattle, there may be mastitis and pneumonia. Diagnosis is made by demonstrating capsulated yeast cells in tissues, spinal fluid, pus or other exudate and confirmed by culture of the pathogen. No reliable treatment is known.

Disease Name. Cryptococcosis (syn. Torulosis, European Blastomycosis Busse-Buschke's disease.)

Pathogen. Cryptococcus neoformans (Sanfelice) Vuillemin, 1901. Syn. Saccharomyces neoformans Sanfelice, 1894; Torulopsis neoformans (Sanfelice) Redaelli, 1931; Debaryomyces neoformans (Sanfelice) Redaelli, Ciferri & Giordano, 1937; C. hominis Vuillemin, 1901; D. hominis Todd & Herrmann, 1936; C. lithogenes (Sanfelice) Vuillemin, 1901; Torula histolytica Stoddard & Cutler, 1916; Torulopsis histolytica (Stoddard & Cutler) Castellani & Jacono, 1933; Torula nasalis Harrison, 1928; Torulopsis neoformans (Sanfelice) Redaelli race nasalis (Harrison) Lodder, 1934; C. nasalis (Harrison) C. W. Dodge, 1935; and probably C. granulomatogenes (Sanfelice) Vuillemin, 1901. (Other synonyms are given by Lodder & Van Rij (1952), p. 374.)

Hosts. Cattle, horse, cat, dog; pig (Vuillemin, 1901), cheetah (Weidman & Ratcliffe, 1934), marmoset monkey (Takos & Elton, 1953), ferret (Skulski & Symmers, 1954). Also man, see Conant et al. (1954), pp. 149–168.

Geographical Distribution.
U.S.A. (Emmons, 1953), Italy (Sanfelice, 1895, cited by Saunders, 1948b), Germany (Westhues & Engelhardt, 1930), France (Vuillemin, 1901), Great Britain (Skulski & Symmers, 1954), Holland (Hammer & Englert, 1956). Worldwide in man.

Symptomatology. In neither man nor animals is the clinical picture of Cryptococcus neoformans infection well defined. C. neoformans shows a predilection for the central nervous system in man and commonly induces a fatal meningitis which, as Cox & Tolhurst (1946) pointed out, can readily be confused with tuberculous and other forms of subacute and chronic meningitis. In some cases the lungs are the site of the primary infection and more rarely the skin involved. Inoculation of experimental animals, especially mice, almost invariably results in severe infection of the central nervous system but spontaneous infections in animals are more varied. Natural infection of the central nervous system is not uncommon (McGrath, 1954) but, as in man, the lungs or skin may be involved, and there are records of bovine cryptococcal mastitis. Most of the records for animals, as for man, have been from the U.S.A. but the widespread incidence of cryptococcosis throughout the world suggests that this may be due merely to the condition being more often correctly diagnosed in North America than elsewhere. For a general summary of cryptococcosis in animals, see Barron (1955), Littman & Zimmerman (1956, Chapt. 6).

Horse. Frothingham (1902) isolated a yeast from a myxoma-like lesion in the lung of a horse from Massachussetts which had shown a persistent nasal discharge and in 1914 Meyer isolated from a myxoma-like nasal growth of a horse in Pennsylvania the organism designated Torula nasalis by Harrison (1928). Schellner (1935) made a similar isolation in Germany and it is probable that all these yeasts and those obtained by Kikuchi (1923) from a horse in Japan and by Weidman (1935) from the lip of a horse in Philadelphia were strains of C. neoformans.

Cattle. In 1901, Sanfelice in Italy isolated from the lymph node of an ox a yeast which he named Saccharomyces litogenes and which Cox & Tolhurst (1946) believed to have been C. neoformans, and Madsen (1942) isolated a Cryptococcus sp. from a similar site in a cow in New York. The most impressive outbreak of bovine cryptococcosis during recent years, however, was of cryptococcal mastitis described in detail by Pounden et al. (1952), Innes et al. (1952) and Emmons (1952) in which, in the course of 12 months, 106 of 235 cows of a Holstein-Friesian herd in Maryland became infected. Fifty-four of the infected animals developed visible abnormality of the udder or milk and in severe cases the udder was greatly enlarged. A similar outbreak involving 50 of a herd of 280 cows was recorded by Simon et al. (1953). Hammer & Englert (1956) recorded C. neoformans as the cause of ulcerative endocarditis in a bull.

Dogs and Cats. Seibold et al. (1953) reported the first canine case, in which the central nervous system was involved and two additional North American cases were noted by McGrath (1954). (See also Schwabe, 1954.) Holzworth (1952) and Holzworth & Coffin (1953) recorded two feline cases in the U.S.A. In the last two the clinical features were those of an upper respiratory disease. Histological examination revealed infiltration of the pterygoid and presphenoid bones by capsulated yeast cells.

Pathology. Affected organs have been seen to have a slimy appearance (Skulski & Symmers, 1954) with much of the tissue structure disorganized by a jelly-like substance. Microscopic examination reveals globose cells 5–20 micra in diameter with occasional buds, each cell having a very wide mucilaginous capsule. The examination of cerebrospinal fluid, pus and other fluids suspected cases of cryptococcosis is facilitated by mounting in Indian ink.

Sections of tissues show the closely packed yeast cells, often without any marked tissue reaction. Innes et al. (1952), studying the bovine udder lesions, found all stages of development to the chronic state in which the epithelium of the acini, ductules and ducts was dissolved leaving only the fibrous framework of the gland. In the lungs of one infected cow they found small tubercle-like lesions with massive infiltrations of large foamy monocytes containing yeast cells, and in the udder lymph nodes catarrh preceded destruction of the lymphoid tissue.

Mycology. C. neoformans is a non-fermenting, non-mycelial yeast which multiplies by single buds. It grows well on malt agar, Sabouraud's glucose agar, or blood agar at 25° to 37°C. (Growth at the higher temperature distinguishes it from related non-pathogenic species.) At first the cells which are 5–20 micra in diameter, are without a capsule but this structure usually develops later in vitro and without fail in vivo.

In young cultures the growth is white or cream-coloured but later it becomes pale brown, mucoid and runs down the slope to collect at the bottom of the tube.

C. neoformans is usually considered to be an asporogenous yeast, the early claims to have demonstrated ascospore formation being discounted by most modern workers, but recently Benham (1955a) believed she had observed ascospores in several strains, from which she concluded that C. neoformans may be the imperfect state of Lipomyces starkeyi.

Serology. In human cases, C. neoformans, perhaps because of the thick capsule, does not appear to sensitize infected individuals at all easily and it is only recently that Neill et al. (1951) were able to demonstrate reactive substances ("soluble antigens") in the spinal fluid and the blood of a patient by means of high titre rabbit antiserum. There are no data on the serology of animal infections.

Epidemiology. Cryptococcosis has a world-wide distribution, but the source of the sporadic infections in man and animals is not fully established. There is no evidence of the spread of infection from one animal to another, and for long an external reservoir of infection was postulated. C. neoformans was first isolated by Sanfelice in 1895 from fruit juices, but most of the subsequent records have been from man or animals. Carter & Young (1950) noted a case of cryptococcosis in a guinea-pig inoculated with the centrifuged deposit from a bulk milk sample during routine tests for tuberculosis, but no clinical symptoms were seen among the cattle concerned. Probably the most noteworthy series of isolates of C. neoformans apparently unconnected with disease, was that obtained by Emmons (1951, 1954) from soil by the inoculation of mice. More recently, by a similar technique but with the addition of penicillin and streptomycin to the suspension used as the inoculum, Emmons (1955c) demonstrated a remarkable association of C. neoformans with old pigeon nests and droppings. C. neoformans was isolated from 63 of 111 specimens examined and the positive specimens came from 16 of the 19 premises from which collections were made. Emmons was unable to detect C. neoformans in the digestive tract of pigeons and the significance of the association of this fungus with these birds is obscure. It is possible that the droppings are a particularly suitable substrate for the saprophytic growth of C. neoformans and that farm animals might contract pulmonary and other infection from such material.

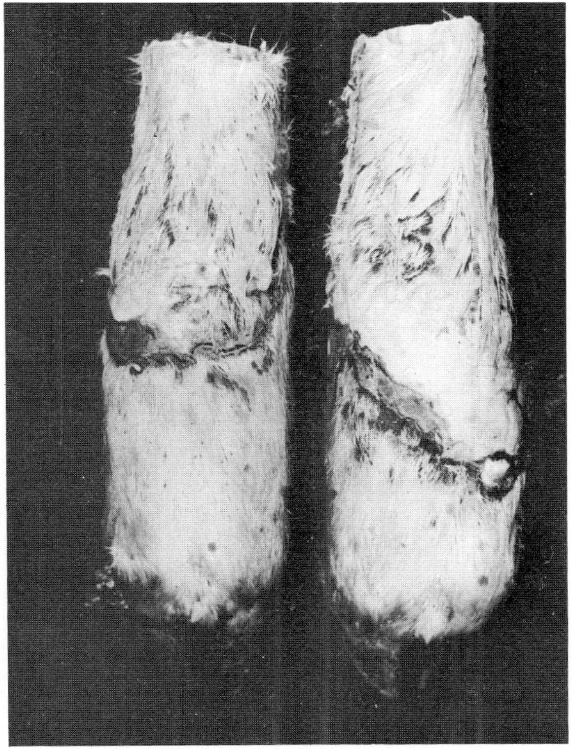

FIG. 9. Ergotism. Gangrenous ergotism (*Claviceps purpurea*) of feet of calf. (Photo: H. T. Davies. Communicated by C. M. Edwards.)

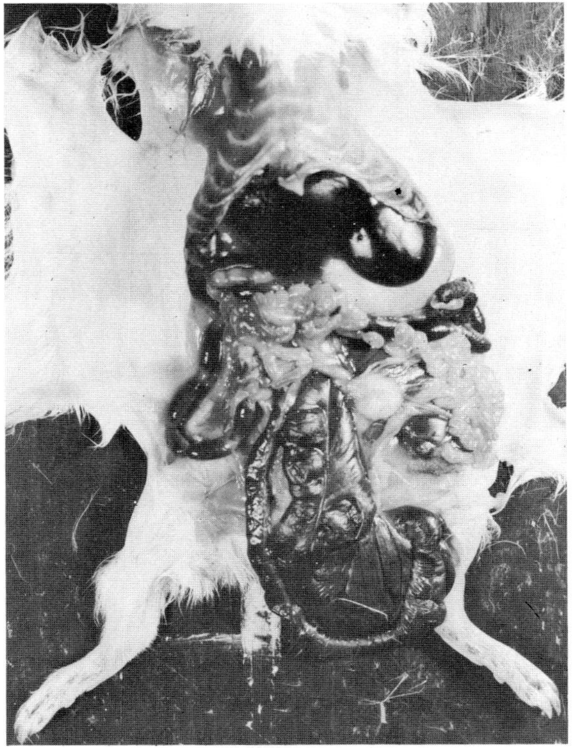

FIG. 10. Mucormycosis. Granulomatous mesenteric lymph node of guinea-pig, (*Absidia ramosa* infection). (Photo: J. S. Paterson.)

PLATE VI

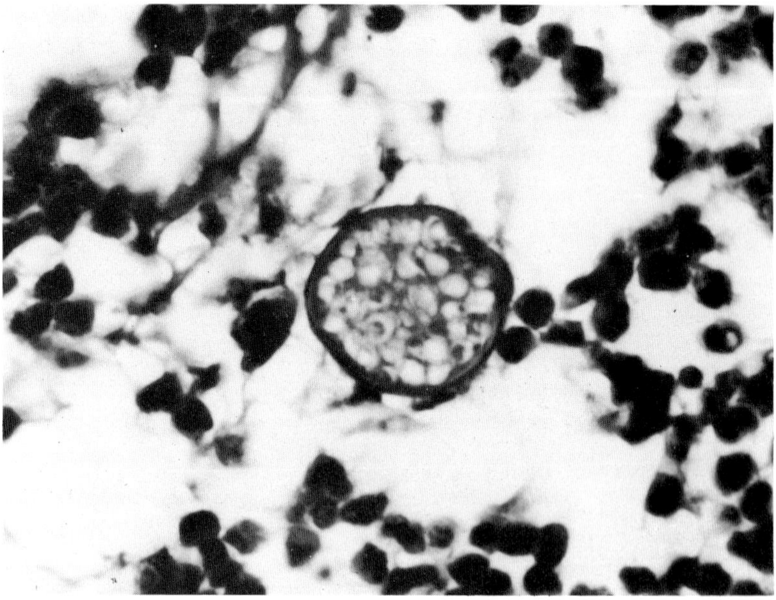

FIG. 11. Coccidioidomycosis. Spherules of *Coccidioides immitis* in lung of man. Stained haematoxylin and eosin. ×700.

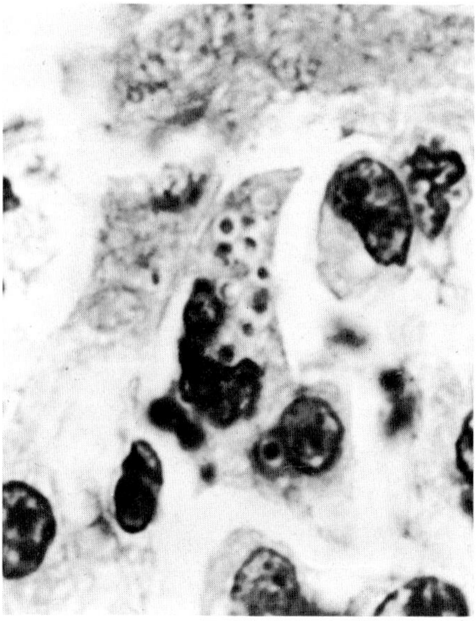

FIG. 12. Histoplasmosis. Yeast-phase cells of *Histoplasma capsulatum* in the liver of a cow. (U.S.A.) Stained haematoxylin and eosin. ×1000. (Photo: R. G. Menges.)

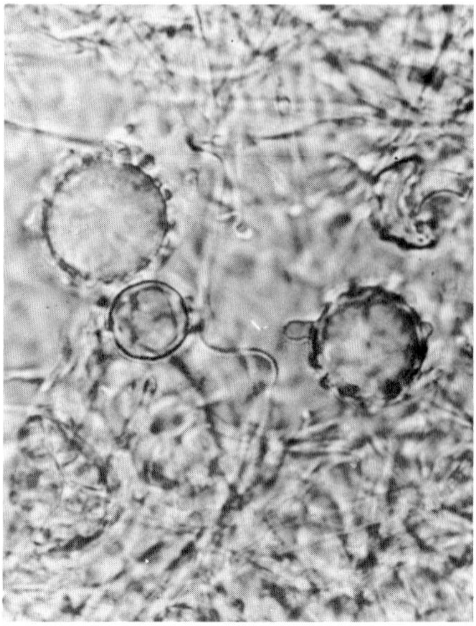

FIG. 13. Histoplasmosis. *Histoplasma capsulatum* chlamydospores in culture. ×500.

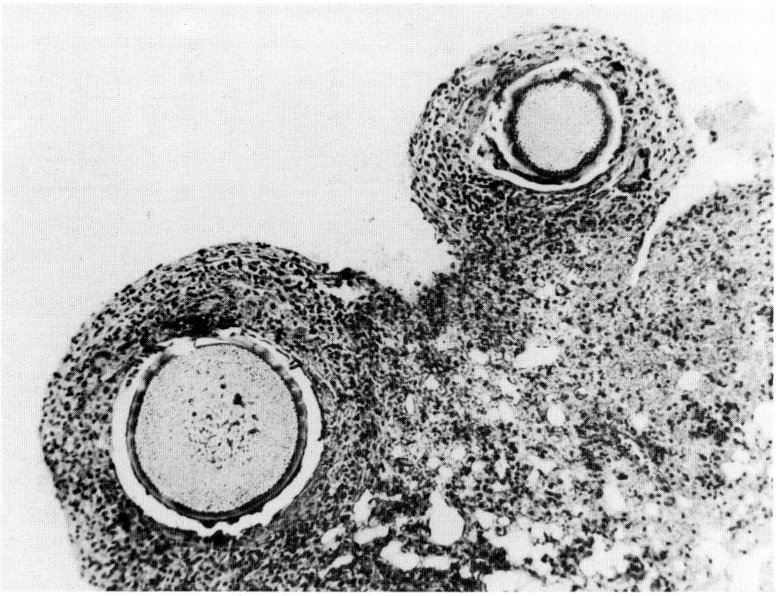

FIG. 14. Haplomycosis. Spherules of *Haplosporangium parvum* in lung of saddle-backed shrew. (Canada.) Stained haematoxylin and eosin. ×60.

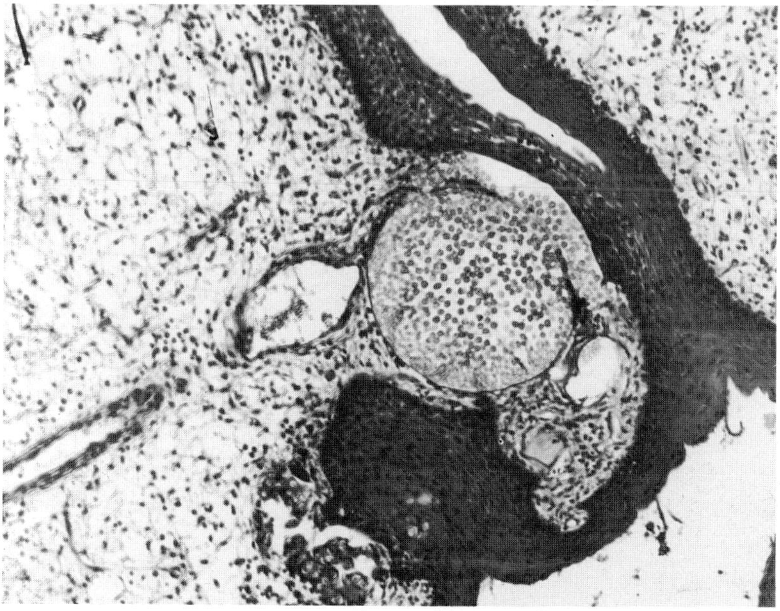

FIG. 15. Rhinosporidiosis. Section of nasal polyp of a horse, showing spherules of *Rhinosporidium seeberi*. (India.) Stained haematoxylin and eosin. ×120.

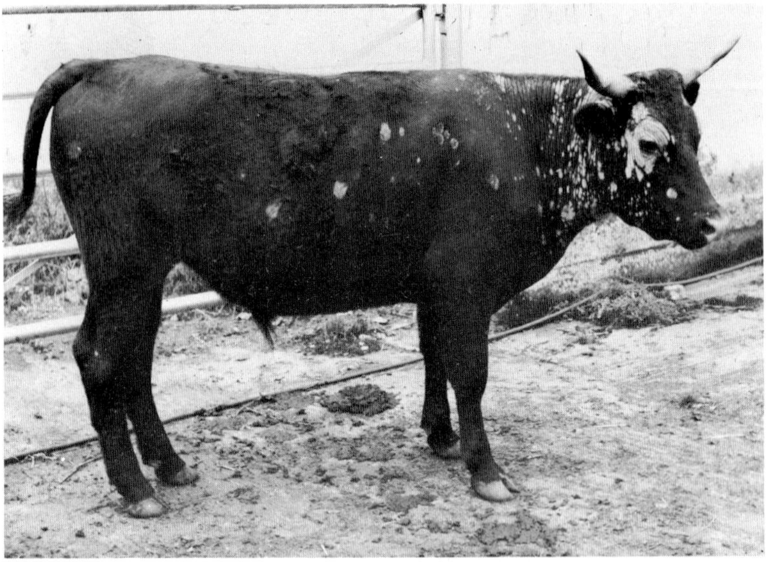

FIG. 16. Cattle ringworm. *Trichophyton verrucosum* infection in a Devon steer.

FIG. 17. Streptothricosis. *Dermatophilus congolensis* infection in a zebu cow. (Dakar, French West Africa.) (Photo: M. Labitte. Communicated by M. G. Thiéry.)

Treatment. There is no known treatment. In the major outbreak of cryptococcal mastitis referred to above the infected animals had to be destroyed. Simon (1955) recorded that ethyl vanillate, polymyxin B and neomycin all inhibited the growth in vitro of C. neoformans from cattle whilst Ségretain et al. (1956) treated affected cows successfully with cycloheximide ("Acti-dione").

Chapter 4

EPIZOOTIC LYMPHANGITIS
(Histoplasma farciminosum)

A chronic infection of horses and other Equidae resulting in a cording of the subcutaneous lymphatics, especially of the limbs and neck, and the development of a series of granulating abscesses, the discharge from which contains yeast-like cells of the pathogen. Infection may also lead to pneumonia and conjunctivitis. Subcutaneous infections respond to surgery and various fungicides. A policy of slaughter in the early stages of an outbreak may be advisable.

Disease Name. Epizootic lymphangitis. (Syn. African farcy (or glanders), Japanese farcy (or glanders), Pseudo-glanders. For other synonyms, see Curasson (1942).) Seuchenhafte Lymphgefässentzündung (Ger.).

Pathogen. Histoplasma farciminosum (Rivolta) Redaelli & Ciferri, 1934. Syn. Cryptococcus farciminosus Rivolta, 1873; Saccharomyces farciminosus (Rivolta) Vuillemin, 1901; Zymonema farciminosum (Rivolta) C. W. Dodge, 1935. For other synonyms, see Dodge (1935) p. 169.

Hosts. Horse, mule, donkey. There is a doubtful record by Oehl (1929) for the pig.

Geographical Distribution.
Endemic in countries bordering the Mediterranean particularly in Italy and North Africa, in East and West equatorial Africa, the Republic of the Sudan, South Africa, and parts of Asia (Japan, China, Indonesia, Burma, India), and the U.S.S.R. Formerly recorded in Sweden, the British Isles, Finland and Germany. The North American records are probably of sporotrichosis (Saunders, 1948). For further details of the geographical distribution see Pallin (1904) and Curasson (1942).

Symptomatology. The clinical picture of epizootic lymphangitis has been described many times (e.g. Pallin, 1904; Curasson, 1942; Plunkett, 1949). Typically there is infection of the subcutaneous lymphatic vessels particularly of the limbs and neck. The infected vessels become dilated at intervals and form lines of hard abscesses (the so-called "cording" of the lymphatics). These abscesses eventually rupture, forming characteristic ulcers from which the discharge of blood-stained pus continues for some weeks until normal healing occurs. By this time further lesions may be found in different stages of development. Lesions may also occur on the mucous membrane of the nostrils and may extend inwards along the septum nasi to the pharynx, larynx and trachea. Bennett (1931) described a primary interstitial pneumonia in mules and horses in the Sudan, which was not associated with skin lesions. In sections of the affected lung tissue an organism closely resembling H. farciminosum was seen, but as no cultural examinations were made its identity is in doubt.

Singh (1956), in India, described in detail the ocular involvement in mules (in 176 of a series of 188 cases). This resulted first in a watery discharge from one or both eyes, some swelling of the eyelids, and later in the development on the conjunctiva and (or alternatively) on the membrana nictitans of papules which became ulcerating button-like growths, the eye becoming closed by a diffuse swelling of the eyelids.

The course of typical lymphatic infections was well described by Bullen (1950–51) from a study of experimental infections. He found that when pus was rubbed into a superficial wound, healing proceeded without any clinical signs of infection. The primary granulating ulcer at the point of inoculation underwent alternating periods of discharge and quiescence until, after 6 to 8 weeks, it had attained a diameter of an inch. The lesion then healed spontaneously and at the end of 2 to 3 months only a scar remained. During this series of events infection had spread along the lymphatic vessels and additional abscesses showing a similar developmental pattern resulted. The protracted nature of the infection is indicated by the figure on p. 25.

Pathology. There seems to be little information available on the pathology of epizootic lymphangitis. According to Bullen (1950–51), the intradermal nodules which are 1–2 cm. in diameter, are confined to the dermis and are freely moveable over the subcutaneous fascia. Subcutaneous nodules developed from inflamed lymphatic vessels draining the affected area may be larger and finally develop into abscesses 2–4 cm. in diameter. In large gland masses the nodules are surrounded by a tough fibrous capsule several centimetres in thickness and containing 30–50 ml. of thick creamy pus. The lymphatic tissue is chiefly involved and the lymphatic ducts are entirely responsible for spread of the infection. Muscles are rarely affected and bone lesions (see Bardelli & Cilli, 1931) are uncommon.

Mycology. A diagnosis of epizootic lymphangitis is made by detecting the many Gram-positive, globose, oval or pear-shaped yeast-like cells (2.5–3.5 x 2.0–3.0 micra) in pus smears and confirmed by culturing the pathogen. Isolation of H. farciminosum has given difficulty and the earlier successful attempts have been summarized by Bullen (1950–51), who used, for primary cultures, Hartley digest agar of pH 7.4 to which 10% horse blood serum had been added, and an incubation temperature of 37°C. On this medium colonies appeared as minute grey flakes after 12 days to 8 weeks. On subculture, H. farciminosum can be grown without difficulty on a number of media, of which Bullen found a modified Czapek–Dox ($NaNO_3$ 3.0 g., KH_2PO_4 1.0 g., $MgSO_4.7H_2O$ 0.5 g., $FeSO_4.7H_2O$ 0.01 g., glucose 40.0 g., peptone (Evans) 20.0 g., glycerol 50.0 g. per litre; pH 6.8) to be particularly suitable.

H. farciminosum is dimorphic, the parasitic phase is yeast-like, the saprophytic phase mycelial and characterized by septate hyphae bearing thick-walled, smooth chlamydospores, 5–10 micra in diameter (cf. H. capsulatum, p. 32). Bullen (1949) was able to effect the mycelial-yeast transformation in vitro by growing the fungus on blood agar at 37°C. in an atmosphere of 15–20% CO_2.

Hemmert-Halswick (1946), reporting on the outbreaks of the disease in Germany during the second world war, observed what were considered to be spores within asci in the mycelial state in culture, and consequently suggested the name Endomyces farciminosus.

Epidemiology. Epizootic lymphangitis is contagious but is confined to Equidae. (Attempts to infect other animals have failed and there is no record of a human infection.) Its onset is insidious and once established it is difficult to eradicate, new cases appearing weeks or even months after infection seems to have been eliminated. These facts are fully established and it may also be noted that the three major outbreaks of epizootic lymphangitis during the twentieth century (in England and Ireland after the South African war, in Europe during the first world war and in Italy, Burma and India during the second) have all been associated with the massing together of large numbers of horses associated with military operations. It is, however, not clear from whence the infection originates and by what agency it is spread. H. farciminosum has as yet been found only in association with diseased animals, but it almost certainly has a saprophytic phase which, perhaps, like that of H. capsulatum, occurs in the soil. It is spread from diseased to healthy animals by contact and by the use of infected harness etc.; and in the latter connexion it may be noted that Bardelli & Ademollo (1927) found the pathogen to be viable and still virulent after natural desiccation in the laboratory for 25 months. Contact or contaminated equipment does not, however, always satisfactorily account for the initiation and course of every outbreak and it appears very probable that a vector plays a part. Experimentally it can be transmitted by intradermal or subcutaneous injection of pus from lesions. Voronov (1949) has noted that in Russia the incidence of epizootic lymphangitis is seasonal. Most new cases appear in the autumn and early winter and as the incubation period is about three months most new infections must occur during the summer months. He offered circumstantial and some experimental evidence that in summer infection is facilitated by biting flies which pierce the skin in order to suck the blood. Stable-flies (unspecified) follow to feed on the exuding blood and lymph and it is these flies that are responsible for the transmission of the disease. Flies had been considered as probable vectors as early as 1914 by Saunders, and later Plunkett (1949) also came to this conclusion. Voronov urges early diagnosis of the disease and the immediate treatment of infected animals so that infection is eliminated before the succeeding summer.

Treatment. Epizootic lymphangitis was eradicated from the British Isles after its introduction at the beginning of the century by a vigorous slaughter policy (Pallin, 1904), and though the disease has never been re-introduced it is still notifiable under the Diseases of Animals Acts. This suggests that slaughter is preferable to treatment in areas in which the disease is not endemic.

No completely satisfactory treatment is known. Early cases may be cured by local surgery followed, according to Plunkett (1949), by the intravenous injection of up to 50 ml. of 1:1,000 mercuric chloride ($HgCl_2$). Mercuric biniodide was used successfully by Parlier (1936) and by Parnes (1938), the latter supplementing the internal treatment with external applications of concentrated lactic acid, copper sulphate, or iodoform.

Hidiroglon (1950) employed the daily intravenous injection of 5 ml. formol in 25 ml. water for 20 days, and a vaccine treatment has been advocated (Palmeiro, 1946).

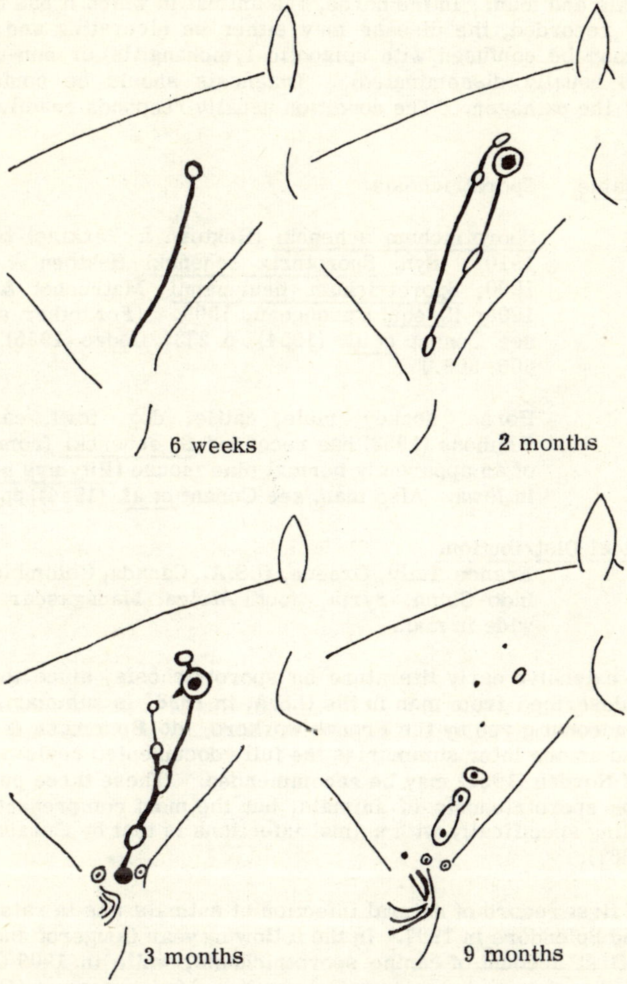

Development of lesions on neck of mule following subcutaneous inoculation of pus. Filled-in areas represent ulcers. After Bullen (1957).

Chapter 5

SPOROTRICHOSIS
(Sporotrichum schencki)

Sporotrichosis, which is widely distributed geographically, affects both animals and man. In the horse, the animal in which it has been most frequently recorded, the disease may either be ulcerating and localized (when it may be confused with epizootic lymphangitis) or non-ulcerating (when it is usually disseminated). Diagnosis should be confirmed by culture of the pathogen. The condition usually responds readily to iodide therapy.

Disease Name. Sporotrichosis.

Pathogen. Sporotrichum schencki (Hektoen & Perkins) Matruchot, 1910. Syn. Sporothrix schencki Hektoen & Perkins, 1900; Sporotrichum beurmanni Matruchot & Ramon, 1905; S. equi Carougeau, 1909. (For other synonyms, see Conant et al. (1954), p. 233; Dodge (1935), pp. 802, 805–808.)

Hosts. Horse, donkey, mule, cattle, dog, fowl, camel, rat. Emmons (1953) has recorded S. schencki from the liver of an apparently normal pine mouse (Pitymys nemoralis) in Iowa. Also man, see Conant et al. (1954), pp. 222–239.

Geographical Distribution.
France, Italy, Greece, U.S.A., Canada, Colombia, Brazil, Indo-China, Syria, South Africa, Madagascar. World-wide in man.

The extensive early literature on sporotrichosis, since the disease was first described from man in the U.S.A. in 1898, is summarized in the classical account given by the French workers de Beurmann & Gougerot (1912), and among later summaries the fully documented reviews by Grütz (1928) and Nordén (1951) may be recommended. These three publications all mention sporotrichosis of animals, but the most comprehensive summary dealing specifically with animal infections is that by Curasson (1942, pp. 258–267).

The first record of natural infection of animals was in rats in Brazil by Lutz and Splendore in 1907. In the following year Gougerot and Caraven gave the first account of canine sporotrichosis, while in 1909 Carougeau described the disease in mules and horses in Madagascar. (For details of these records, see de Beurmann & Gougerot, 1912.) Subsequently there have been further accounts of sporotrichosis in Equidae: Chaillot (cited by Curasson, 1942) recorded sporotrichosis in the camel in Syria, Sparapini (cited by Saunders, 1948b) noted cases in the domestic fowl in Italy, and a possible case in cattle was provided by Humphreys & Helmer's (1943) isolation of a species of Sporotrichum from pulmonary lesions in a cow in Canada. The records of sporotrichosis in animals are, however, far outnumbered by those in man and there is still need for a critical study of animal infections.

Symptomatology.

Horse, Donkey, Mule. The classical expression of sporotrichosis in man is a series of chronic subcutaneous nodules. The initial lesion is typically of an extremity, usually the hand, from which infection spreads via the lymphatic vessels, which become corded, to give a series of secondary nodules along the limb. Sooner or later the nodules ulcerate and discharge pus. Dissemination of the infection is unusual and the viscera are rarely involved. In the horse [Peppler & Twiehaus, 1942; Jones & Maurer, 1944 (U.S.A.); Albornoz, 1945 (Colombia); Rannaud, 1950 (Indo-China); Thorold, 1951 (S. Africa)], donkey [Wendt, 1941 (U.S.A.)], and mule [Piratininga, 1943 (Brazil); Olson, 1947 (U.S.A.), Matthéakis, 1953 (Greece)] the typical infection resembles that in man (de Beurmann & Gougerot, 1912). In horses, in addition to infection involving the lymphatics of the limbs and the cervical region, Watson (1920) described a non-ulcerating and disseminated form in which the lymphatics are not infected.

Dog. While lymphatic infection may occur in the dog, involvement of the bones and the internal organs (liver and lungs) with fatal results appears to be more frequent than in other hosts (de Beurmann & Gougerot, 1912; Collet, 1934).

Mycology. The diagnosis of sporotrichosis is best confirmed by culture of the pathogen which is usually effected without difficulty by the inoculation of slopes of Sabouraud's glucose agar with pus from an unopened lesion and incubation at laboratory temperature; within a week flat, moist, and usually whitish colonies develop. Microscopic examination reveals septate hyphae bearing groups of globose or pear-shaped conidia (2–4 x 2–6 micra) terminally on unbranched conidiophores. The parasitic phase is yeast-like and the pathogen therefore dimorphic, and the yeast phase can be induced in vitro by inoculating slopes of Francis' cystine agar or brain-heart infusion agar and incubating at 37°C. Examination of the pasty growth which results shows it to be non-mycelial and to be composed of budding cells.

The appearance of different isolates in culture at laboratory temperature may vary very considerably, particularly as regards pigmentation, some being non-pigmented while others develop abundant dark brown to black pigment with age. Such differences have led to the differentiation of several species, but recently Lurie (1948, 1950, 1951) — who cited earlier work on the mycology of species of Sporotrichum — showed that isolates of a number of 'species' (including S. equi) could not be distinguished nutritionally or serologically from one another, thus supporting the view that sporotrichosis in both animals and man is caused by a single species, S. schencki.

Rats, mice and hamsters are the experimental animals of choice. Mice (see Baker, 1947) are particularly sensitive. On intraperitoneal inoculation they develop peritonitis and the pathogen can be readily demonstrated at Gram-positive, cigar-shaped cells in pus smears and in tissue sections.

Immunity. Both Lurie (1948) and Nordén (1951) described methods for the production of anti-Sporotrichum serum in rabbits. Nordén (1951) recorded the results of an investigation on the diagnosis of sporotrichosis in man by agglutination, complement-fixation, and precipitin tests which he found, in a short series of cases, to be of limited value. The precipitation test seemed to be the most sensitive.

Pathology. Although the histopathology of human lesions has often been described (e.g. Conant et al., 1954) there is much less information regarding animal infections. de Beurmann & Gougerot (1912) described canine lesions and Jones & Maurer (1944) dealt with the pathology of equine sporotrichosis. In experimental sporotrichosis in mice, Baker (1947) noted polymorphonuclear infiltration within five days of inoculation at the site of intraperitoneal injection, which was followed by invasion of the liver and spleen in which large numbers of yeast-phase cells could be seen within macrophages. Death usually occurred at two and a half to three and a half weeks, and in survivors the lesions became encapsulated, often containing no organisms. As with man, the pathogen is difficult to detect in tissue sections of naturally infected animals and also in the discharge from lesions. The visual absence of the pathogen from pus is a useful point for the differential diagnosis of sporotrichosis from epizootic lymphangitis (see p. 23), in which the pus contains numerous yeast cells.

Infection of man usually results, sooner or later, in the development of a skin hypersensitivity to antigens prepared from the pathogen or from culture filtrates, but the evidence suggests that this effect also is of limited value in diagnosis.

There seems to be no information on the serology of natural infections in animals.

Epidemiology. Sporotrichosis in both animals and man has a world-wide distribution and is of sporadic incidence. It is not contagious — although Carougeau in Madagascar in 1909 (see de Beurmann & Gougerot, 1912) did record one instance of transmission from a mule to a veterinary surgeon who operated on it — and, in sharp contrast to epizootic lymphangitis, equine sporotrichosis does not become epidemic. The primary infection can often be traced to a wound, and cases in man are most frequent among those engaged in horticulture or agriculture. This pattern clearly indicates that sporotrichosis is an exogenous infection, and it has long been realized that the reservoir of infection is infected plants and plant debris, while more recently S. schencki has been isolated from soil by Emmons (1953) and others.

Benham & Kesten (1932) successfully infected carnations and other plants with S. schencki, and Mackinnon (1949a) was able to forecast the occurrence of a group of human cases in Uruguay from the incidence of hot humid weather which presumably encouraged the growth of the fungus on its natural substrates and so increased the chances of man contracting infection. The largest outbreak of human sporotrichosis ever recorded was that among gold miners in South Africa during 1942–43, when the infection was traced to growth of the pathogen on timber in humid mines.

It is probable that similar factors operate in the epidemiology of sporotrichosis in animals, but the hosts are perhaps less susceptible than is man.

Treatment. Sporotrichosis in animals, as in man, responds well to the administration (either orally or intravenously) of potassium iodide.

Chapter 6

HISTOPLASMOSIS
(Histoplasma capsulatum)

Histoplasmosis, which has a world-wide distribution, is either a generalized and fatal or, more usually, a localized and benign infection of animals (especially dogs and wild rodents) and man. The pathogen shows a predilection for the reticulo-endothelial system, but other tissues may be affected. It is diagnosed by demonstrating the small yeast-like cells in infected tissue and by isolation of the pathogen in culture. Infection results in a persistent skin hypersensitivity. No satisfactory treatment is known.

Disease Name. Histoplasmosis.

Pathogen. Histoplasma capsulatum Darling, 1906. (For synonyms, see Conant et al. (1954) p. 139.)

Hosts. Dog, cat, cattle, horse, (sheep, pig and fowl have been recorded as histoplasmin positive); rat, mouse, woodchuck, skunk, opossum, grey fox (Emmons et al., 1955); ferret (Levine et al., 1938); African monkey (Courtois et al., 1955); for additional animal hosts see Collier & Winckel (1952). Also man, Conant et al. (1954), pp. 119–149.

Geographical Distribution.
Endemic in man in the U.S.A. (central Mississippi valley, Ohio valley, Appalachian mountains, etc.) and perhaps tropical Africa and elsewhere; sporadic cases have been reported from many countries (see Emmons, 1955a). Recorded from animals in the U.S.A., Panama (Tomlinson & Grocott, 1945), Surinam (Collier & Winckel, 1952), Brazil (Pará, 1946; Silva & Paula, 1956), France (Courtois et al., 1955), Turkey (Akün, 1950), India (Shortt, 1923).

Symptomatology. H. capsulatum was first described in 1906 from man in Panama by Darling, who believed the pathogen to be a protozoon. The next human case was from the U.S.A. in 1934, when de Monbreun demonstrated the mycotic nature of the infection. From subsequent records from the U.S.A. and elsewhere it appeared that histoplasmosis was a relatively rare, disseminated, and usually fatal mycosis. Recently, however, it has become clear that in certain parts of the U.S.A. the incidence of histoplasmosis is high and that, like coccidioidomycosis, it is typically a mild, or even subclinical, infection. Many apparently normal individuals in the endemic areas give a positive reaction to histoplasmin (an antigen prepared from the pathogen, see p. 32) and a number who are histoplasmin positive show pulmonary calcifications in spite of the fact that they are tuberculin negative.

Dog. de Monbreun, in 1934, infected puppies experimentally

with *H. capsulatum*, and five years later he recorded the first natural infection in a dog (de Monbreun & Anderson, 1939), which was also the first record of *H. capsulatum* from an animal. Since then many more cases of canine histoplasmosis have been recorded (mostly in the U.S.A.) (see Schwabe, 1954) and 42 of these records have been usefully summarized by Menges (1951a). There is no characteristic clinical picture for histoplasmosis in dogs. In 25 of the cases reviewed by Menges for which the data were available the most frequent symptoms were gradual loss of weight, emaciation, persistent diarrhoea, anorexia, enlarged abdomen, and hepatomegaly. Fever, anaemia, vomiting and other non-characteristic abnormalities were more rare. Pneumonic infiltrations may be detected by X-rays (Menges *et al.*, 1950) and at *post-mortem* examination intrapulmonary nodules may be found. These are either soft and caseous or apparently calcified (Rowley *et al.*, 1954). The incidence of the disease did not seem to show any correlation with sex or breed, but the majority of the cases occurred in dogs three years old or younger. Most of the cases reported by Menges were disseminated and fatal. Menges *et al.* (1950) reported a non-fatal experimental *H. capsulatum* infection in a dog and Emmons *et al.* (1955) isolated *H. capsulatum* from 145 of 397 apparently normal dogs in Loudoun County, Virginia.

Cat. There are fewer records of histoplasmosis in cats, in which the disease is similar to that in dogs. Akün (1950) recorded a feline case in Turkey and Emmons *et al.* (1955) in Virginia isolated *H. capsulatum* from 81 of 449 cats examined.

Cattle. Most of the evidence for the incidence of bovine histoplasmosis is the circumstantial evidence afforded by the histoplasmin test. Among the few cases in which *H. capsulatum* has been demonstrated is the one reported by Menges & Kintner (1951) from Missouri of an Aberdeen Angus cow which, after a period during which it did not gain in weight, showed difficulty in breathing, diarrhoea and swelling of the brisket a week before it was slaughtered.

Horse. For equine, as for bovine, histoplasmosis the proven cases of infection are rare and the clinical symptoms are not well known. Richman (1948) recorded histoplasmosis in a horse in Tennessee which had lesions of the lungs and bronchial lymph nodes and Randall *et al.* (1951) detected *H. capsulatum* in the apparently normal amnioallantoic membrane and in the spleen of a horse in the same State.

Pathology. The tissue response to *H. capsulatum* infection is typically a marked hyperplasia of the reticulo-endothelial system, but other tissues may be affected. Giemsa-stained smears of blood, bone marrow, sputum, or material from lymph nodes show yeast-like cells 3–5 micra in diameter within mononuclear blood cells and macrophages on microscopic examination with an oil immersion objective. Frequently, diagnosis is only made *post mortem* when sections of organs such as the spleen, liver or lungs show massive infiltration by similar small yeast-like cells which are indistinguishable from those of *H. farciminosum* (the cause of equine epizootic lymphangitis, see p. 22) so that in horses the diagnosis of histoplasmosis must be confirmed by culturing the pathogen.

Mycology. H. capsulatum is dimorphic. The parasitic phase is yeast-like, the saprophytic phase at laboratory temperature mycelial. In tissues the small yeast cells referred to above multiply by simple budding. In culture on Sabouraud's glucose agar or on other media there is abundant aerial mycelium, which is at first white and later buff-coloured and which bears two types of spores: (1) small globose or somewhat pyriform conidia, 2.5–3.0 micra in diameter, which are either sessile or borne singly on short stalks and either smooth or echinulate, and (2) larger, globose, thick-walled chlamydospores with prominent tuberculations on the surface. The chlamydospores are a diagnostic feature.

If grown at 37° C. on a cysteine-containing medium such as brain-heart infusion blood agar (or other media, see Titsworth & Grünberg, 1950) the growth becomes yeast-like and similar to the parasitic phase and the transformation from the mycelial to the yeast form and vice versa can be effected at will.

Isolations are made by inoculating both brain–heart infusion blood agar and Sabouraud's glucose agar (with or without the addition of penicillin and streptomycin) and incubating the first at 37° C. (when any growth of H. capsulatum will be yeast-like) and the second at room temperature (when the growth will be mycelial). Isolations from grossly contaminated material or from soil may be made, as described by Emmons (1949), using mice, which are very susceptible to H. capsulatum.

While mice and other laboratory animals are susceptible to both the mycelial and the yeast phase of the pathogen it is usually most convenient to make experimental inoculations with the yeast phase by the intraperitoneal route. Dogs may also be infected by feeding.

Serology. As already mentioned, a characteristic feature of infection by H. capsulatum is the development of a persistent skin sensitivity to an antigen prepared from the pathogen, and as the reaction has been much used and much studied the method may be taken as a standard for similar skin testing in connexion with other mycotic infections.

The basic procedure is the preparation of a standardized filtrate from a culture of the pathogen on liquid medium. For H. capsulatum this filtrate is designated histoplasmin. Histoplasmin, suitably diluted, is injected subcutaneously into the animals to be tested and the reaction, if any, noted after 24 or 48 hours.

Salvin & Hottle (1948) studied factors which influence histoplasmin formation and they obtained the maximum yield of histoplasmin on the glucose/asparagine medium used by Smith (1943) for coccidioidin production (see p. 39) after 8–10 weeks' growth at 25° C. with an initial pH of 7.0–8.0 and a surface to volume ratio of near unity; the filtrate being standardized against a preparation of histoplasmin of known titre either by the complement-fixation test (Salvin, 1947) or by intradermal tests on rabbits and guinea-pigs (Emmons et al., 1945).

The method of testing animals is described by Menges (1951b) who advocates making the test in the cervical area for cattle, horses, dogs and cats; near the base of the left ear for pigs; the left lower eyelid for sheep; and the left wattle for poultry. The procedure is to clip the hair (as necessary) from the test area, swab it with 70% alcohol and then to inject 0.1 ml. of histoplasmin (undiluted - 1:10 for larger animals and poultry; 1:10 - 1:1000 for cats and dogs) intradermally by means of a 1 ml. tuberculin syringe with a quarter-inch 25 to 27 gauge intradermal needle. The test is read after 48 hours by observing and palpating any induration or thickening and by measuring the horizontal diameter of the induration. A reaction is considered to be positive when there is a definite induration 5 mm. or more in diameter.

Epidemiology. Although the literature of histoplasmosis is very extensive (see the reviews by Ruhe & Cazier (1949) and Emmons (1955a) of histoplasmosis of animals and man, respectively) there are still many gaps in the knowledge of the disease and uncertainties regarding the epidemiological significance of a number of the ascertained facts.

It is generally agreed that histoplasmosis is not contagious (healthy mice introduced into a group of infected animals do not contract the disease), that it has an exogenous origin, and that there are clearly delimited geographical regions in which it is endemic. In endemic regions the incidence of infection, as indicated by histoplasmin testing, is high in both man and animals. In Kansas, Missouri, and Iowa, Menges (1954) recorded sensitivity rates of 5% for cattle, 73% for horses, 33% for sheep, 1% for pigs, and 1% for chickens. He also recorded a 14% incidence in a random sample of 102 dogs from Kansas and Missouri but detected 5 reactors in 26 dogs associated with cases of histoplasmosis in man or dogs, while Furcolow & Ruhe (1949) found a close similarity between reaction rates of children and cattle of successive age groups of one to seven years, an observation which strongly suggests that man and cattle are exposed to a common source of infection.

Emmons, Bell & Olson (1947) and others have shown that wild rodents are not uncommonly infected by H. capsulatum but it is believed that these animals do not constitute a reservoir of infection and that they too are exposed to the common source of infection which is probably the soil. H. capsulatum was first isolated from the soil by Emmons (1949), whose findings have been repeatedly confirmed, and it now appears that H. capsulatum has a wide but apparently rather localized distribution in soil. The causes of the localization are not clear. Zeidberg (1955) has published data which indicate that the percentage of positive histoplasmin reactors is significantly higher in regions with red-yellow podzolic soils (20.1 as compared with 4.6%). Earlier, Zeidberg et al. (1952) had shown a marked association of H. capsulatum with the soil of chicken runs, and particularly of disused chicken houses; an observation that has been confirmed by others including Menges, Furcolow & Habermann (1954) who have given a detailed account of an outbreak affecting both man and animals on a Kansas farm and originating from a disused chicken house. Loosli et al. (1952) recorded a rather similar outbreak in six members of a farm family who probably acquired infection when removing sawdust from a silo. Larsh,

Hinton & Cozad (1956) have drawn attention to the higher incidence of H. capsulatum in soils of sheltered or protected areas than in soils from open sites (6 and 3%, respectively) and point out that this finding is not incompatible with what is known about the temperature and humidity growth-requirements of the fungus.

Treatment. No satisfactory treatment is known.

Chapter 7

NORTH AMERICAN BLASTOMYCOSIS
(Blastomyces dermatitidis)

A chronic infection of animals (especially dogs) and man which is endemic in North America (especially the eastern half of the U.S.A.). Pulmonary involvement is typical. The disease is diagnosed by detecting spherical yeast-like cells with 'double-contoured' walls in infected tissues and exudates, and by culturing the pathogen. Iodide therapy and, during recent years, the administration of stilbamidine have proved effective in human cases.

Disease Name. North American Blastomycosis. Syn. Blastomycosis (pro parte in veterinary literature), Gilchrist's disease.

Pathogen. Blastomyces dermatitidis Gilchrist & Stokes, 1898. Syn. Gilchristia dermatitidis (Gilchr. & Stokes) Redaelli & Ciferri, 1934, Zymonema dermatitidis (Gilchr. & Stokes) C. W. Dodge, 1935. For other synonyms see Dodge (1935), p. 168.

Hosts. Dog, horse. Also man, see Conant et al. (1954) pp. 45–74.

Geographical Distribution. U.S.A.

Symptomatology. North American blastomycosis was first recognized by Gilchrist in 1894, and four years later the pathogen was described and named by Gilchrist and Stokes, who were able to infect experimentally a sheep, a horse, and two dogs. In man the disease may be either cutaneous (when the infection is often of long standing) or systemic when, until recently, most cases had a fatal termination. In animals the systemic form is the most usual.

Dog. Canine blastomycosis was first recognized in 1913 by Meyer. Ramsey & Carter (1952) reviewed the 16 cases published up to 1950 from the U.S.A. (Illinois, Ohio, N. Carolina, Iowa) and additional cases have been recorded since by Robinson & Schell (1951), Robbins (1954), and Newberne et al. (1955).

The syndrome most usually observed is that of a chronic debilitating and fatal disease, the onset of which is insidious. There are usually extensive pulmonary lesions. More rarely the skin (Saunders, 1948a) or other tissues are involved.

Horse. Benbrook et al. (1948) recorded a case in a 6-year-old mare, in which the disease was diagnosed post mortem by the histological examination of the udder. For ten months before death there was a series of abscesses in the region of the anus and vulva and during the last few weeks a rapid loss in weight.

Pathology. Infection by B. dermatitidis typically results in the production of granulomatous processes and these give the lungs of an infected dog a characteristic mottled appearance of greyish-white and pink. Diagnosis of blastomycosis is made by detecting in the pulmonary exudate or in tissue sections spherical cells, 8–12 micra in diameter, which may or may not show simple budding. The cells have thick refractile walls which give them a 'double-contoured' appearance. Ramsey & Carter (1952) described the pulmonary lesions in a dog as infectious granulomata with peripheral increase of reticulo-endothelial cells and fibroblasts. Later stages were characterized by mononuclear and giant cell reaction, with the yeast cells present in large numbers in the centre of the lesion. Robbins (1954) found exudative lesions on the larynx and the mammary glands, and proliferative granulomata composed of epithelioid and giant cells with mild fibrosis in the lungs and other organs.

Mycology. B. dermatitidis is a dimorphic fungus for which temperature is the phase-determining force. Growth at 37°C. is yeast-like, while at 25°C. it is mycelial. The usual recommendation is to culture infected material on blood agar or beef infusion agar at 37°C. and on Sabouraud's glucose agar at 25°C., when the pathogen can be isolated without difficulty. The mycelial growth is white and cottony and bears two types of conidia: (1) sessile, globose, 3–4 micra in diameter, borne near septa, and (2) globose to pyriform, 4–5 micra in diameter, borne terminally on unbranched conidiophores.

Mice and guinea-pigs are both suitable as experimental animals.

Serology. In man blastomycosis induces a skin sensitivity to an antigen (blastomycin) prepared from the pathogen, and the sera of infected individuals will fix complement with suspensions of the yeast phase or with blastomycin. Such tests are not, however, specific for there is some cross reaction with histoplasmin (see p. 32). The serology of animal infections does not appear to have been studied.

Epidemiology. Blastomycosis is not contagious. In dogs there appears to be no correlation of infection with age, sex or breed, but most of the canine cases have occurred in the geographical region where the incidence of human blastomycosis is highest. In man, male labourers are most commonly infected and, as pointed out by Chick et al. (1956), the evidence available clearly indicates that North American blastomycosis is exogenous and suggests that the source of infection is some natural substrate such as the soil. B. dermatitidis has not, however, been isolated from soil. Ramsey & Carter (1952) noted a fatal case in which a veterinary surgeon apparently contracted infection while performing an autopsy.

Treatment. Prognosis of systemic blastomycosis in animals is grave and no therapeutic measures can be recommended. In human cases iodide therapy and the administration of stilbamidine have proved very successful (see Conant et al., 1954). Heilman (1952) has reported the effects of stilbamidine on experimental blastomycosis in mice.

PLATE IX

FIG. 18. Aspergillosis. Opened left abdominal air-sac of hen showing *Aspergillus fumigatus* sporing, with lung lesions above).

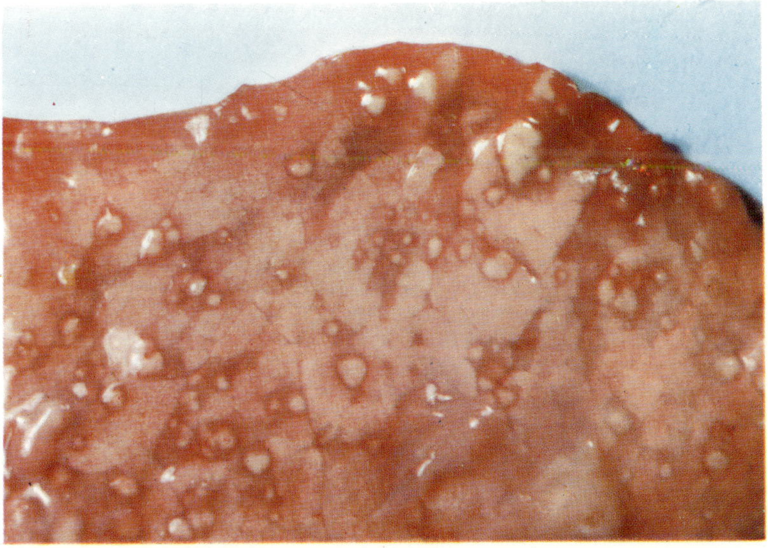

FIG. 19. Aspergillosis. Lung of piglet (*Aspergillus fumigatus* infection).

PLATE X

FIG. 20. Moniliasis. Oesophagus of piglet (*Candida albicans* infection).

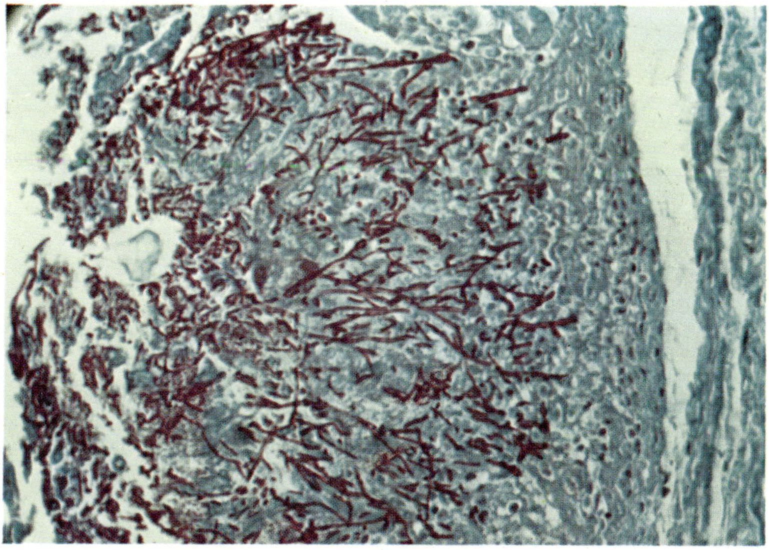

FIG. 21. Moniliasis. Section of lesion in cardiac zone of stomach of piglet. Stained periodic acid-Schiff. ×500. (Photo: J. T. Done.)

Chapter 8

COCCIDIOIDOMYCOSIS
(Coccidioides immitis)

A soil dust-borne infection of domestic and wild animals and man which is endemic in arid regions of North and South America. It is sometimes disseminated, progressive and fatal but usually localized and benign. Diagnosis is indicated by the development of a positive skin reaction to an antigen prepared from the pathogen and is confirmed by demonstrating 'spherules' of the fungus in tissues or exudates and by culture. No satisfactory treatment is known.

Disease Name. Coccidioidomycosis. Syn. Coccidioidal granuloma, Oidiomycosis.

Pathogen. Coccidioides immitis Rixford & Gilchrist, 1896. (A partial list of synonyms is given by Conant et al. (1954) p. 110.)

Hosts. Cattle; dog; sheep (Beck, 1929 and Maddy, 1954b – in slaughtered animals); and various wild animals, e.g. desert rodents (especially Perognathus spp.) (Emmons, 1942, 1943); Townsend mole (Scapanus townsendii)(Rector & Rector, 1948); cottontail rabbit (Sylvilagus floridanus) (Turn & Eveleth, 1954); European rabbit (Kemenes, 1954); mountain gorilla (Gorilla beringeri) (McKenney et al., 1944); American monkey (H. A. Smith, 1948). Also man, Conant et al. (1954), pp. 93–118.

Geographical Distribution. Endemic in arid parts of the south-western States of the U.S.A., (California, Arizona, Texas, and neighbouring States), northern Mexico, Honduras, Venezuela and the Chaco region (parts of Bolivia, Paraguay, and Argentina) of South America. Animal infections have been recorded from the U.S.A. and Hungary.

Symptomatology. Coccidioidomycosis was first recognized in the eighteen-nineties as a chronic and usually fatal disease of man. During the past 15 years it has, however, become increasingly apparent that the most usual manifestation of C. immitis infection in man is an acute, self-limiting, and therefore benign, pulmonary infection which confers a life-long skin sensitivity to an antigen prepared from the pathogen. Both these clinical aspects are exhibited by animals.

Cattle. In cattle the infection is usually benign. Typically, there is a granulomatous involvement of the bronchial and mediastinal lymph nodes. More rarely the lungs are attacked (Davis et al., 1937). Infection in cattle was first recorded by Giltner (1918) in a cow from the San Joaquin Valley, California (one of the noted endemic centres for the disease in man) and since then more than three thousand cases have been reported in cattle from the same State (Maddy, 1954a). Prchal (1948) recorded 503 cases among 38,175 cattle slaughtered at Phoenix, Arizona, and many other records have been made by meat inspectors.

Dog. There appears to be no characteristic clinical picture of coccidioidomycosis in the dog (Jasper & Lewis, 1951), but the infection seems to be more frequently disseminated than in cattle. There are reports of involvement of the lungs, liver, spleen and kidneys (Farness, 1940) and in several other cases the bones have been affected. Cordy & Hoop (1953) reported a case in which the mandible, left radius and ulna were involved and subsequently Hage & Moulton (1954) gave a fully illustrated account of four cases in each of which there was infection of the ribs, vertebral segments, pelvis and long bones in addition to lymph nodes. In three animals the liver, and in one the lungs and the brain were also infected.

Pathology. In most cases of animal infection the diagnosis has been either made or confirmed by histological examination of tissues obtained at autopsy. Such tissues show thick-walled spherical structures ('spherules') 20 to 60 micra or even more than 100 micra in diameter, each of which contains numerous small globose endospores (2–5 micra in diameter). Similar structures may be found by the direct examination of pus from abscesses, spinal fluid, etc., and they are diagnostic. Confusion with the much larger sporangia of Rhinosporidium seeberi (see p. 45) is unlikely and the spherules can usually be distinguished without difficulty from the cells of Blastomyces dermatitidis (see p. 36) by their larger size, the absence of budding, and the endospores. Differential diagnosis of the spherules from those of the southern strain of Haplosporangium parvum (see p. 42) is not so easy but according to Breslau (1955) this may be accomplished by staining to show the characteristic chitin in the cell wall of C. immitis and the cellulose in that of H. parvum.

The granulomatous lesions of coccidioidomycosis in bovine lymph nodes are generally encapsulated with central caseation. Epithelioid and giant cells with occasional accumulation of polymorphonuclear cells are frequently seen, and sometimes the central mass becomes calcified (Maddy, 1954a). In a dog, Langham (1955) reported generalized lesions in which the spherules were surrounded by histiocytes and peripheral neutrophiles.

Mycology. C. immitis is a dimorphic fungus. In animal tissues it is regularly non-mycelial and multiplies by spores produced in sporangia (spherules). In culture under special conditions on a serum–chick embryo medium, spherules have been obtained in vitro by Lubarsky & Plunkett (1955) but when cultured on the usual media the growth is mycelial, spherule production does not occur, and reproduction is by means of small, thick-walled rectangular to barrel-shaped spores from 2.5–3 micra broad and from 4–5 micra long, which are produced in chains in which spores alternate with short lengths of empty hypha. These chlamydospores are produced in exceedingly large numbers. They are very easily detached and are highly infective so that cultures of C. immitis have to be handled with the greatest care. Flooding the culture with sterile saline before making subcultures is one precaution advocated. Petri dish culture should be avoided and all discarded cultures must be carefully autoclaved. In spite of such precautions laboratory infections are not uncommon (Looney & Stein, 1950) and are occasionally fatal.

Isolations are easily made by culture on Sabouraud's glucose agar (with or without the addition of penicillin 20 units/ml. and streptomycin 40 units/ml.) and incubation at 25°C., when moist greyish colonies first appear in three to four days. Later abundant aerial mycelium is produced. When making isolations from heavily contaminated material, Georg et al. (1951) have advocated the addition to the medium of cycloheximide ("Actidione") at a concentration of 0.5 mg./ml.

Both mice (Friedman et al., 1955) and guinea-pigs are very susceptible experimental animals. Mice are usually inoculated intraperitoneally with a saline suspension of chlamydospores. Male guinea-pigs within a week of intratesticular inoculation develop a marked orchitis, when fluid may be withdrawn for examination. (For detailed accounts of C. immitis, see Baker et al. (1943), Emmons (1947)).

Immunology. Infection by C. immitis and subsequent recovery results in a resistance to re-infection and this immunological response is accompanied by a sensitivity of the skin to an antigen prepared from the pathogen, a phenomenon which has been much studied in man because of its use in diagnosis and in epidemiological studies. The antigen (coccidioidin) used is a suitably processed filtrate from a culture of C. immitis and the medium most favoured has been one devised by C. E. Smith (1943) which has the following composition: l-asparagine, 14.0 g.; magnesium sulphate ($MgSO_4,7H_2O$), 1.5 g.; dipotassium phosphate (K_2HPO_4), 1.13 g.; sodium citrate, 0.9 g.; ferric citrate (scales), 0.3 g.; glycerol, 25.0 g.; glucose, 10 g.; distilled water to 1,000 ml. 0.1 ml. of a standardized preparation, either undiluted or suitably diluted, is injected as for the histoplasmin test (see p. 32).

Although on occasion it is a useful supplementary diagnostic test, a positive skin reaction to coccidioidin, like a positive tuberculin test, is not of course evidence of an active infection and usually merely indicates a past infection. In regions where the disease is endemic almost all the adult population are positive reactors. There has been comparatively little coccidioidin testing of animals, but the data available suggest that the response patterns shown by populations of animals are likely to resemble those of man.

Epidemiology. Coccidioidomycosis is apparently not contagious for either man or animals and for man the evidence clearly points to air-borne infection and to the soil as the source of the pathogen. In regions where the disease is endemic, new infections are most frequent during the dry summer months and after dust storms, and during the second world war the incidence of coccidioidomycosis among troops sent for training to these arid areas was reduced by grassing airfields and spraying dusty roads with oil. Further, there are a number of records of the isolation of C. immitis from soil in the south-western States of the U.S.A. (see Emmons, 1953). When Emmons (1942, 1943) discovered the high incidence of C. immitis infection among desert rodents, he suggested that they might constitute a basic reservoir of infection and that it was these diseased animals which maintained the infectivity of the soil. In support of this view he noted that while the incidence of the disease is high in certain species it is low in others (even in some susceptible to experimental infection) and that the geographical distribution of coccidioidomycosis might be determined by the distribution of susceptible species of rodents. The infection is often chronic in susceptible rodents, but infected animals are able to breed. As Emmons pointed out, the evidence that C. immitis is primarily a parasite of rodents rather than a saprophytic soil fungus is inconclusive. The nutritional requirements of C. immitis are not exacting and by analogy with haplosporangiosis (see p. 41)) and histoplasmosis (see p. 33) for which animal reservoirs of infection seem less likely, it is possible that rodents, farm and domestic animals and man are exposed to the same hazard of infection from a soil fungus of limited distribution.

Treatment. The benign form is self-limiting and treatment is unnecessary, while no satisfactory treatment is known for the progressive form of coccidioidomycosis in man, and the same applies to animals. Vogel et al. (1954) have recently claimed some success in the artificial active immunization of guinea-pigs against respiratory challenge with C. immitis.

Chapter 9

HAPLOMYCOSIS
(Haplosporangium parvum)

Haplomycosis is a respiratory disease of burrowing mammals. The causal fungus is found as large thick-walled spherules in the lung tissue. In artificial culture it is mycelial. It is possible that haplomycosis plays a part in the fluctuations of natural populations of small mammals. Haplosporangin sensitivity has been reported in man and cattle.

Disease Name. Haplomycosis. Syn. Haplosporangiosis.

Pathogen. Haplosporangium parvum Emmons & Ashburn, 1942.

Hosts. Many species of rodents, insectivores, herbivores and carnivores including beavers (Castor canadensis) and moles (Talpa europaea).

Geographical Distribution. North America (Emmons & Ashburn, 1942; Dowding, 1947a; Bakerspigel, 1956); Europe – England (McDiarmid & Austwick, 1954; Tevis, 1956), Sweden (Jellison, 1956), Italy (Ciferri, cited by Bakerspigel, 1956); Asia – Korea (Jellison, 1954).

Emmons & Ashburn (1942) first isolated and named Haplosporangium parvum from wild rodents in Arizona, during a systematic study of the epidemiology of coccidioidomycosis. The spherules of H. parvum in the lungs closely resembled those of Coccidioides immitis and some difficulty was experienced in the histological differentiation of the two pathogens. Double infections were found in some animals. Subsequently other authors have shown that H. parvum is widely distributed in the Northern Hemisphere and is probably a 'soil inhabitant'.

Symptomatology. Almost all the records of haplomycosis have been made from animals trapped or shot in the field and therefore assumed to be healthy. Typically the affected lungs show occasional or numerous light grey to yellowish lesions throughout the tissue, sometimes protruding from the surface. Lesions have not been reported in any other organs.

Pathology. Large spherules may be seen with the naked eye lying within a narrow reaction zone forming a thin capsule. When this covering is ruptured the spherule is released and may be used for isolation, after washing in sterile water.

In the early stages of experimental infection, according to Ashburn & Emmons (1945), the spherules were 5–10 micra in diameter and enclosed by small collections of mononuclear cells. After a further two weeks they were 25–30 micra in diameter with walls 3–4 micra thick and were surrounded by mono- and polymorphonuclear leucocytes. Giant cells were rarely seen in quantity until four months after infection, and some fibrosis was also apparent at this time.

Mycology. The spherules of H. parvum germinate in 4–5 days at 25°C. with the production of a large number of germ tubes. Colonies are generally white to buff-coloured, and Carmichael (1951) distinguished four types according to the amount of surface mycelium. Large numbers of small round conidia, 2.5–5.0 micra in diameter, are produced singly or in groups on the ends of short conidiophores arising at right angles to the main hyphae. Except in certain strains mycelial growth does not occur at 37°C., but conidia incubated at this temperature undergo enlargement and wall-thickening to form chlamydospores up to 26 micra in diameter, similar to the lung spherules (Carmichael, 1951).

Jellison (1950) commented on the smaller size of the spherules from Arizona animals (about 14 micra in diameter) as compared with those from rodents in Alberta (Dowding, 1947a) and Montana (up to 400 micra in diameter). In experimental studies, Carmichael (1951) found that these sizes were maintained in inoculated animals and also that the southern strains mostly gave floccose colonies whilst those of northern strains were generally granular in texture. The former were also more heat resistant, only forming chlamydospores at 40°C.

Intranasal instillation of spore suspensions into anaesthetized mice was found by Ashburn & Emmons (1945) to be the most successful method of inoculation. Guinea-pigs, rats, hamsters and monkeys were less susceptible than mice. In no case did a progressive infection develop and no evidence of multiplication of the fungus in the lungs was found. Using subcutaneous inoculation of guinea-pigs, Carmichael (1951) produced small nodules at the sites of injection within 2–10 days and these persisted for up to seven months. Each nodule consisted of an abscess or small granuloma and contained large numbers of spherules each derived directly from an injected spore.

The relationship of H. parvum with other pathogenic fungi was reviewed by Dowding (1947b), who considered it to be closely related to Blastomyces dermatitidis. Carmichael (1951) agreed with this suggestion and gave evidence of the similarity of the conidiophore and conidial morphology and development in the two fungi. He also considered that H. parvum does not belong to the genus Haplosporangium Thaxter, or even to the Phycomycetes. A more suitable disposition must await a better understanding of related members of the Moniliaceae.

Serology. Skin sensitization in man was originally described by Emmons & Ashburn (1942) and has also been demonstrated by Paynter (1954). It has been reported in cattle by Menges & Habermann (1954) but no infections have been found in either host. Ashburn & Emmons (1945) found that prior infection by H. parvum did not give protection against Coccidioides immitis and that no cross-sensitization occurred between the two species.

Epidemiology. Dowding (1947b) noted that H. parvum grew well on sterilized soil and it has since been isolated from natural soil by Menges & Habermann (1954). There seems no doubt that burrowing animals become infected by the inhalation of spores from mycelium in the soil. The relationship of H. parvum infection to the periodic fluctuations in the mole population in Britain was discussed by McDiarmid & Austwick (1954), who concluded that many factors were involved, including the presence of a pathogenic aerobic actinomycete and of nematodes in the lungs of almost all the moles examined.

Chapter 10

RHINOSPORIDIOSIS
(Rhinosporidium seeberi)

Rhinosporidiosis is a chronic, non-fatal infection of cattle, horses and mules in warmer countries; it is characterized by the development of nasal polyps. Diagnosis is confirmed by finding many large sporangia in the diseased tissues. The standard treatment is surgical excision of the growths.

Disease Name. Rhinosporidiosis.

Pathogen. Rhinosporidium seeberi (Wernicke) Seeber, 1912. Syn. Coccidium seeberia Wernicke in Belou, 1903; R. kinealyi Minchin & Fantham, 1905; R. equi, Zschokke, 1913; R. ayyari Allen & Dave, 1936; R. amazonicum Aben-Athar, 1944; and possibly Desmosporidium hylarum Carini (1940) on the tree-frog Hyla rubra.

Hosts. Cattle (Rao, 1938; Robinson, 1951), horse (Ayyar, 1932; Sahai, 1938; Prieto & Pires, 1944), mule (Quinlan & de Kock, 1926; Bueno & Faria, 1941). Also man, see Conant, et al. (1954), pp. 253–262.

Geographical Distribution.
Endemic in India (Rao, 1938); sporadic in South Africa (Zschokke, 1913; Quinlan & de Kock, 1926), Uruguay (see Saunders, 1948b), Brazil (de Mello, 1949), Argentina (Prieto & Pires, 1944), U.S.A. (Robinson, 1951), ? Australia (Albiston & Gorrie, 1935), and elsewhere in man (de Mello, 1949).

Symptomatology. In animals the site attacked is the mucous membrane of the nose and the infection is unilateral. According to Rao (1938), in cattle and horses the tumours are rarely larger than 2–3 cm. in diameter and may either be pedunculated or sessile. They are lobulated, soft, pink in colour, bleed readily, and are dotted with small white specks (the sporangia). In man the nasal polyps are similar but often larger, and other sites including the pharynx, larynx, eye, ear, skin, vagina and rectum may be infected.

Pathology. Sections of a growth show papillary processes of the epithelium beneath which the sporangia are embedded in a delicate fibrous or fibro-myxomatous tissue. The sub-epithelial tissue is very vascular and there is infiltration with polymorph cells, eosinophiles, and red blood cells. Giant cells are rare.

Mycology. Rhinosporidium seeberi is exceptional among fungi pathogenic for animals and man in that attempts to culture it have either been inconclusive (Rao, 1938) or unsuccessful. It was at first thought to be a protozoon and, though its status as a fungus is now generally conceded, its exact taxonomic position remains very doubtful. Knowledge of the life-history of R. seeberi is derived from the monograph by Ashworth (1923), whose detailed studies were based on a human case, but there is now general agreement that the same species attacks both man and domesticated animals. The literature was reviewed by de Mello (1946).

The sporangia originate from small globose cells 6–7 micra in diameter. These increase in size and, on attaining a diameter of approximately 100 micra, become transformed into sporangia by the deposition of a layer of cellulose within the chitinous wall and by the division of the contents into approximately 16,000 spores which eventually escape from the sporangium (now 200–300 micra in diameter) via a special pore.

The mycological diagnosis is made by finding sporangia in wet mounts and in stained tissue sections of polyps, and spores in the nasal discharge. The large size of the sporangia allows them to be easily distinguished from the much smaller 'spherules' of Coccidioides immitis, and their thin walls from those of Haplosporangium parvum. There is little likelihood of their confusion with other fungal structures.

Epidemiology. Attempts to induce experimental infection with spores from nasal discharge have failed (de Mello, 1949) and there is no evidence of transmission from one animal to another or to man. The mechanism of infection is not known, neither has the source of the infection been established. It does, however, seem probable that injury plays a part in determining infection and that infection is sometimes from air-borne soil particles. Rao (1938) noted the association of rhinosporidiosis with lesions of nasal schistosomiasis. The latter disease may be differentiated in cattle and buffaloes by the finding of the characteristic eggs of Schistosoma nasalis in the nasal discharge or in sections of the lesions. Rao also considered that bullocks were more frequently infected than cows and noted that in all except one of the 18 cases of rhinosporidiosis in bullocks which he studied in the Madras Presidency the animals were four to nine years old. It is at about three and a half years of age that bullocks have the nasal septum punctured for the nose string and are set to the plough. Infection was commonly recorded on the margin of the string hole. Cows are rarely used for ploughing and rarely have the nasal septum punctured. It is interesting to note that the incidence of rhinosporidiosis is higher among men than women (and as women rarely follow the plough it seems possible that both men and bullocks are subject to the same hazard of dust-borne infection when ploughing) and to recall that Mandlik (1937) observed an association between the incidence of rhinosporidiosis in man in the Poona district and the use of certain wells and water tanks subject to inundation during rain.

Treatment. The standard treatment is the surgical excision of the infected growths which may, however, reappear a year or more after the operation. Successes have been claimed in human cases by the administration of trivalent and pentavalent antimony preparations as an adjunct to surgical measures.

Chapter 11

MUCORMYCOSIS

(Species of Mucor, Absidia and Rhizopus)

Mucormycosis is a little-known disease of animals caused by pathogenic species of Mucor, Absidia and Rhizopus. The lesions are either granulomatous or ulcerative and both types may occur in the same animal, the former occasionally becoming generalized. The organs chiefly attacked are the lymph nodes of the alimentary canal and the gastric and intestinal mucosae. Affected lymph nodes enlarge and become caseo-calcareous with many small foci containing hyphae. The nodular lesions closely resemble aspergillosis but mucormycotic ulcers are clinically distinct. Diagnosis is made on the presence of mucoraceous hyphae in the lesions and the isolation of the fungus. Inoculation of spores of the fungi into experimental animals leads to the generalized or chronic granulomatous form of the disease.

Disease Name. Mucormycosis, including Mycotic Ulceration.

Pathogens.
*Absidia corymbifera (Cohn) Sacc. (Vink, 1941).
Syn. A. lichtheimi Lendner.
Absidia ramosa (Lindt) Lendner (Christiansen, 1922).
Mucor javanicus Wehmer (Porges et al., 1935).
*Mucor pusillus Lindt (Tscherniak, 1928).
Mucor racemosus Fresen. (Frank, 1890).
Mucor spinosus van Tieghem (Nielsen, 1902-03).
*Rhizopus cohnii Berl. & de Toni (Nielsen, 1929).
Syn. R. suinus Nielsen; Mucor rhizopodiformis Cohn).
*Rhizopus microsporus van Tieghem (Christiansen, 1922).
Syn. R. equinus Cost. & Lucet.

*pathogenic for experimental animals

Hosts. Cattle (Gleiser, 1953), pig (Christiansen, 1922), horse (Tscherniak, 1928); dog (Rivolta, 1885; Gleiser, 1953), mink (Momberg-Jörgensen, 1950), guinea-pig (Ainsworth & Austwick, 1955a), mouse (Symeonidis & Emmons, 1955).

Geographical Distribution. Europe and North America.

Although the pathogenicity of mucoraceous fungi for experimental animals has been known since the work of Lichtheim (1884), spontaneous mucormycosis in animals has rarely been reported, only some forty contributions appearing in the literature. The early accounts are concerned with the disease in man (Paltauf, 1885) and are of limited value owing to their lack of adequate descriptions, so that it is impossible to be certain whether the fungi concerned were in fact mucoraceous at all. To some extent the characteristics of the lesions described are a guide, but isolation of fungi was not often accomplished. When the species was identified it invariably proved to be non-pathogenic, e.g. Mucor racemosus (Frank, 1890). For this reason no reliable account of mucormycosis in animals has been located before that of Christiansen (1922) who described two cases in pigs. Subsequently the disease has been defined in several domestic animals and differentiated from other granulomatous and ulcerative diseases. The disease is now recognized as of regular, if sporadic, occurrence in the Northern Hemisphere.

Symptomatology. Mucormycosis is chiefly known as a granulomatous disease generally involving the lymph nodes. As it rarely produces any signs until either the granulomata become visible as protuberances or the animal wastes away most of the reported cases in pigs and cattle have been discovered during routine inspection in abattoirs.

The cases on record fall into two distinct types, both of which may be acute or chronic in nature. The type most frequently reported is characterized by the occurrence of large granulomata which have apparently developed in the mesenteric, bronchial, mediastinal, or submaxillary lymph nodes. Similar lesions have also been found in the liver, lungs and kidneys. The other form of the disease, from which apparently no fungus has yet been isolated, is the ulceration of the alimentary canal, chiefly the stomach and intestines. Animals of all ages appear to be attacked but this type of acute ulceration has been described only in young animals.

Pigs. About fifteen cases of the granulomatous type of disease have been reported in pigs and two thirds of these have been described by Christiansen (1922, 1929). In each case tumour-like growths replaced the mesenteric lymph nodes and in one instance the mass weighed 1.5 kg. Additional lesions included the involvement of the submandibular lymph node in one pig, the presence of a granulating ulcer in the small intestine in another and the formation of embolic tumours in the liver and lungs in two other pigs. In Vink's (1941) case the left inguinal and submaxillary lymph nodes were swollen to the size of a tennis ball and contained a watery, blood flecked, inodorous fluid with yellowish detritus. Tscherniak (1934) described two cases of gastric ulcers in pigs in which he found mucoraceous hyphae, but both animals were considered to have died from subacute swine fever, and Walkiewicz (1934) found three further severe cases. Tumour-like lesions in the liver were described by Hoogland (1932) and haemorrhagic infarction in the kidneys was associated with haematuria.

Cattle. Gleiser (1953) first mentioned the occurrence of caseo-calcareous lesions in the bronchial and mediastinal lymph nodes of a yearling heifer and Davis et al. (1955) found similar lesions in eleven cattle during meat inspection. The most frequent lesions were in the mesenteric lymph nodes and lungs and consisted of a greenish-yellow caseocalcareous mass with a variable amount of scar formation. None of the animals had shown any apparent symptoms of disease.

Abomasal ulceration has been the more frequently reported form of bovine mucormycosis and most likely accounted for a proportion of the early literature on peptic ulcers in animals. Sanchez-Botija (1951) first found mucoraceous hyphae in a single ulcer 5–6 cm. diam. in an ox, whilst Gitter & Austwick (1957) summarized seven acute cases in young calves, stressing that these represented every case of abomasal ulceration seen in 208 consecutive post mortem examinations of calves. All except one of the calves died following the onset of severe scouring and one to several ulcers up to 4 cm. in diam. were found on each occasion. The early lesions were small, raised, inflamed foci which developed into ulcers with raised haemorrhagic margins and grey, depressed, necrotic central areas. The role of mucoraceous fungi in bovine mycotic abortion is discussed on p. 54.

Horse. The few references to mucormycotic infection in the horse are not very satisfactory from the mycological standpoint. Frank (1890) for instance isolated the non-pathogenic Mucor racemosus from a subcutaneous tumour on the withers of a horse, and Costantin & Lucet (1903) named an isolate from a horse Rhizopus equinus (= R. microsporus) but failed to give any indication as to whether or not the horse was suffering from a disease. An interesting condition was found by Nielsen (1902/03) in a ten-year-old horse which had a sero-fibrinous, yellowish-green discharge from the right nostril, accompanied by swelling on the nose and in the submaxillary lymph nodes. On trephining the right frontal bone he uncovered a greyish-white fatty mass consisting chiefly of the mycelium of Mucor spinosus. This finding may indicate that infection by the nasal route, postulated for the orbital and cerebral forms of mucormycosis in man by Baker (1957) may also occur in animals. Possibly the only true mucormycotic lesion reported in horses is the nodule seen by Tscherniak (1928), from which he isolated Mucor pusillus.

Dog. Although an early report of a nasal infection in a dog was made by Rivolta (1885) this paper has not been available and Gleiser's (1953) two cases are the only well-documented ones. In one of these the left kidney was enlarged and entirely granulomatous; in the other an ulcer 2 cm. in diam. was found in the stomach, with granulating processes extending into the muscularis. Both animals had wasted and developed convulsions before death. Cultures were not obtained in either case.

Mink. Momberg-Jörgensen (1950) gave a detailed account of nine cases in a mink farm in Denmark. The first signs of infection were ulcerating subcutaneous nodules on the neck, shoulders and back, which healed and later broke out again. Death took place up to two months after the appearance of symptoms but a number of animals recovered. In each of the four cases examined post mortem there was extensive involvement of the subcutaneous and skeletal muscles and Absidia corymbifera was isolated in two instances.

Guinea-pigs. The outbreaks of benign mucormycosis in guinea-pigs reported briefly by Ainsworth & Austwick (1955a, b) occurred at a research establishment and were first discovered when animals were being abdominally palpated for the early detection of the enlarged mesenteric lymph nodes found in pseudotuberculosis (Pasteurella pseudotuberculosis infection). Material from many enlarged and caseated lymph nodes was plated out but Absidia ramosa or A. corymbifera invariably appeared in pure culture. Direct examination of the lymph nodes showed mucoraceous hyphae in the lesions. The guinea-pigs involved were mostly 3–6 weeks old, the enlarged lymph nodes appearing just after weaning; although no symptoms were noted in the first outbreak, in a later one diarrhoea, enteritis and typhlitis occurred, whilst occasional deaths took place in adult animals. Generally recovery was spontaneous and over the age of six weeks only scar tissue remained.

Fowl. No authentic case of mucormycotic infection has been found in birds. Bollinger (1880) isolated Mucor racemosus from the air-sac of birds, but Neumann (1909) considered this to have been an error in determination, so that it seems likely that the disease was actually aspergillosis. Porges et al. (1935) obtained M. javanicus from the inflamed gizzard of unthrifty chickens which were dying in large numbers, but again it is not clear whether this fungus was actually growing in the lesions. Similarly Ainsworth & Austwick (1955b) reported Absidia corymbifera from a hen with a "systemic disease" but no further details were available. There is no apparent reason why mucormycotic infection should not be found in birds, and careful observation of the many instances of isolations of mucoraceous fungi from internal lesions should lead to the confirmation of the disease.

Mouse. Subcutaneous tumours in two mice caused by Absidia corymbifera were reported by Symeonidis & Emmons (1955) during cancer research experiments. One lesion was 3 cm. across and grossly resembled a mammary tumour.

Pathology.

Granulomatous lesions – This type of lesion is normally white, yellow or sometimes haemorrhagic and may either be solid or contain a fluid-filled cavity. The size reported has ranged from a few millimetres across to that of a human head. Generally hyphae may be easily seen on direct examination by teasing out small pieces of the necrotic or caseous area of the lesion in water or in 10% potassium hydroxide, and applying gentle pressure to the coverslip. Davis et al. (1955) recommend the use of a touch-press for this examination. The hyphae are characteristically 2–7 micra wide, freely branching, irregular in outline with numerous swellings and even with occasional cross-walls, although septa are not regarded as a mucoraceous feature.

In structure the granulomata apparently vary according to the species of animal and the organ attacked, and also with the age and speed of development of the lesion. Early subcutaneous lesions in the mink were considered by Momberg-Jörgensen (1950) to consist of a marginal zone of epithelioid cells together with a few plasma cells, lymphocytes, polymorphonuclear cells and fibroblasts with Langhans type giant cells enveloping the hyphae in the central area. No eosinophiles were seen in these lesions. The chronic lesions in the lymph nodes of pigs were described by Christiansen (1929) as being composed of collagen fibres, lymphocytes, plasma cells, giant cells and many eosinophiles, the last-named being a feature also noted by Davis et al. (1955) in cattle. Necrosis of the central areas eventually takes place and calcification and the formation of a fibrous capsule may be the final stage of development (Pallaske, 1939). The kidney lesions described in a dog by Gleiser (1953) also showed giant cell formation and extensive necrosis.

Ulcerative lesions -- The lesions in the abomasum of calves described by Gitter & Austwick (1957) invariably showed the early development of extensive necrosis of the gastric mucosa with the hyphae apparently penetrating from the surface down both the villi and the crypts. Oedema of the muscularis mucosae and the submucosa was accompanied by the infiltration by polymorphonuclear cells and eosinophiles, whilst the muscle layer of the stomach wall directly beneath the lesion was usually thickened. The blood vessels of the submucosa were congested and invaded by hyphae. Christiansen (1929) reported a tumour-like surround to an intestinal ulcer in a pig, and recent cases examined with similar lesions (Austwick, unpublished) have shown the development of granulomata in the submucosa and muscularis of the stomach wall. It seems probable that this represents the progression of the ulcer from the acute to the chronic state.

Disintegration of the hyphae in the central part of the lesions has been observed by Momberg-Jörgensen (1950) and most certainly indicates the death of the fungus. Similar degenerating hyphae have been observed in regressing lesions in guinea-pigs (Ainsworth & Austwick, unpublished).

Mycology. The least satisfactory aspect of mucormycosis in animals is the mycological one. Although the presence of mucoraceous hyphae in what are undoubtedly characteristic lesions is a very strong indication of infection by such fungi, the literature contains only about eleven proven cases in which the causal organism was isolated. The fungus has normally been recovered by plating out pieces of the granulomata on to a suitable medium. Most pathogenic mucoraceous fungi grow well at 37°C. on the sugarless media used for the primary isolation of bacteria and are thus in contrast to many of the saprophytic species which are essentially "sugar fungi". Isolation may be carried out on blood, nutrient, or serum agar, 2% malt agar or Sabouraud's glucose agar, all preferably with the addition of antibacterial antibiotics. Growth generally occurs within 24 hours, is at first fluffy and white, but is soon followed by the formation of sporangia which show specific variation in colour.

The mucoraceous fungi compose a group (the order Mucorales) of the Phycomycetes and are characterized by their non-septate (coenocytic) hyphae, the formation of spores endogenously within a sporangium, and a sexual reproduction involving the fusion of two hyphae to form a thick-walled zygospore. The genera are distinguished on the morphology of the different structures produced in culture. In Mucor the globose sporangia occur singly or in groups along prostrate hyphae whereas in Absidia they are borne in groups by arching, stoloniferous hyphae which arise from behind the advancing margin. Rhizopus resembles Absidia but the sporangiophores arise only at the points of contact of the stolons with the medium.

Mucor pusillus is the only Mucor species conclusively shown to be pathogenic. It was obtained by Tscherniak (1928) from a horse, by Baudet (1932) from a pig, and by Ainsworth & Austwick (1955b) from the brain of a calf. This species does not grow well below 30°C. but produces a greyish-brown felt-like colony with erect, branched sporangiophores on most media at 37°C. The sporangia are 50–80 micra in diameter and the spores round, smooth and 2–4 micra in diam. M. racemosus (Frank, 1890) is a common, most probably non-pathogenic, saprophyte, which does not grow well at 37°C. Cultures are woolly and light brown in colour with sporangia 30–60 micra in diam. and round to oval spores 3–10 micra in diam. Characteristic golden-brown, thick-walled chlamydospores (10–25 x 10–15 micra) are found in the hyphae. The two Absidia species differ from each other only in the size and shape of their spores. In A. corymbifera they are round, smooth, 2–5 micra in diam. and in A. ramosa oval 4–5 x 2–3 micra. Both species have characteristically pear-shaped sporangia which dehisce around the upper part on the columella and are thus distinct from the Mucor spp. in which the remains of the sporangium wall is left as a basal collarette. Rhizopus produces rather more robust sporangiophores and sporangia which frequently have thick brownish walls. The two species known to be pathogenic for animals R. cohnii and R. microsporus have many synonyms and the group is in urgent need of revision together with the two other species R. arrhizus and R. oryzae known only from man but pathogenic for experimental animals. The sporangia of both R. cohnii and R. microsporus are 50–100 micra in diam. but the spores of the former are 5–6 micra in diam. and of the latter 3–4 micra in diam., both being round to oval, smooth or angular, greyish and generally longitudinally striate.

The chief taxonomic work on the Mucorales is the rare monograph of Zycha (1935) which includes descriptions of all the known species. Another important study is that of Naumov (1939), whilst much useful information on the pathogenic species is given by Dodge (1935).

Serology and treatment. There seems to be no information on the serology of mucormycosis, and no form of treatment has been attempted.

Epidemiology. No reliable data are available on the epidemiology of mucormycosis and it can only be suggested that infection occurs following the inhalation or ingestion of spores from feedingstuffs. Isolations of fungi from hay samples and from the air of cowsheds and stables (Rolle & Kolb, 1954; Ainsworth & Austwick, 1955b) have shown the preponderance of potentially pathogenic mucoraceous fungi in the environment of farm animals. Pulmonary lesions are thought to arise from the inhalation of very large quantities of spores but the frequency of gastric and intestinal lesions suggests that entry through the alimentary canal may be of major importance. Certainly mucoraceous fungi may be regularly isolated from the gut contents of animals. The secondary infection of ulcers produced by physiological disorders has been put forward as an explanation of the ulcerative type of mucormycotic lesion but there is no satisfactory evidence to support this view. The possibility of a nasal route of infection has already been discussed.

In an outbreak of mucormycosis, the methods of control which might be applied would be similar to those recommended for aspergillosis, i. e. the removal of the source of the spores as for instance mouldy hay. However this method is obviously of limited use because Paterson (personal communication, 1954) has related how an outbreak of mucormycosis in guinea-pigs occurred following the feeding of a batch of hay of first class quality.

Experimental. Lichtheim (1884) first showed the pathogenicity of mucoraceous fungi for rabbits, long before any natural infections were found. He described how he injected the spores of Rhizopus cohnii (as Mucor rhizopodiformis) which he had obtained from mouldy bread, intravenously into rabbits. These developed lèsions in the kidneys and the lymphoid tissue of the intestines. Lindt (1886) found that two more species, Mucor pusillus and Absidia ramosa were capable of causing lesions in rabbits but it was then nearly forty years before Christiansen (1922) described the first spontaneous cases of mucormycosis in pigs. In the mean time the pathogenicity of R. microsporus (as R. equinus) had been established by Costantin & Lucet (1903) and later Christiansen (1929) produced nodules by the subcutaneous inoculation of A. ramosa spores in guinea-pigs although he found that the intravenous inoculation of a pregnant sow had no effect. Experiments by Bauer et al. (1955) and by Elder & Baker (1956) with Rhizopus oryzae have shown some features of the association of alloxan diabetes with mucormycosis, the two diseases having been associated in man for a very long time.

FIG. 22. Mycotic dermatitis. Clun Forest ewe; wool loss and black pigmentation of skin following infection by *Dermatophilus dermatonomus*.

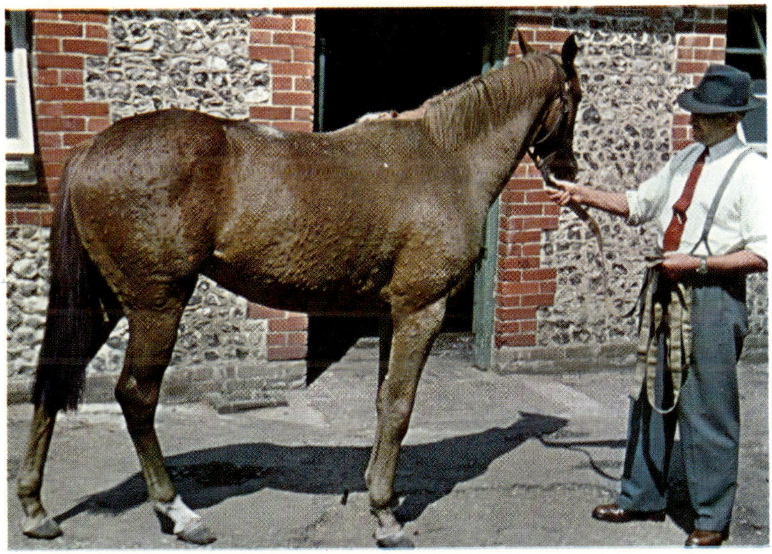

FIG. 23. Horse ringworm. Encrusted and suppurative lesions on the skin of a Thoroughbred, caused by *Trichophyton equinum*.

PLATE XII

FIG. 24. Mycotic abortion. Portion of bovine placenta with thickened cotyledons infected with *Aspergillus fumigatus*.

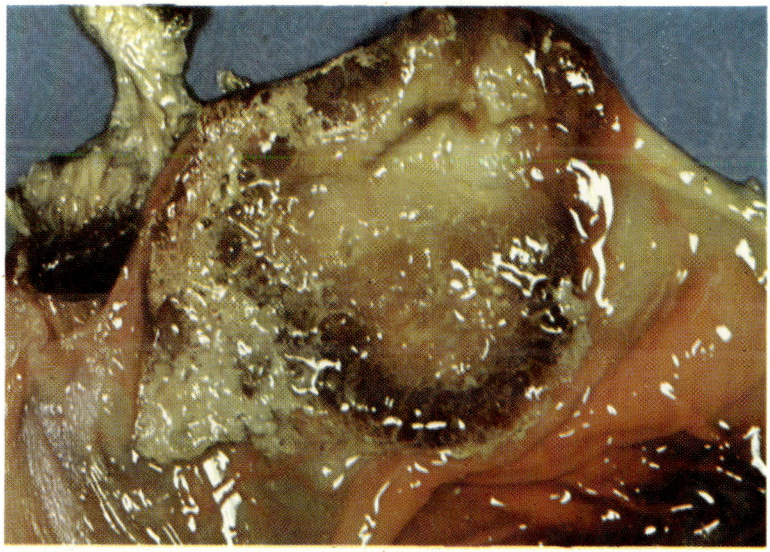

FIG. 25. Mucormycotic ulceration. Stomach ulcer in piglet from which *Rhizopus microsporus* was isolated.

Chapter 12

BOVINE MYCOTIC ABORTION

(Species of Aspergillus, Absidia, Mucor and other moulds)

Bovine abortion associated with fungi has been reported from North America and Europe. Diagnosis is made on the presence of hyphae in the thickened and necrotic placental cotyledons, in the intercaruncular areas, and in the foetal stomach contents. Occasionally skin lesions are present on the foetus. Infection is thought to be primarily respiratory and to be derived from spores in mouldy hay and straw. Placental infection probable takes place by haematogenous spread with an incubation period of one to two months. The condition has been experimentally reproduced by the intravenous injection of spores. No treatment is known but recovery of the dam appears to be spontaneous.

Disease Name. Bovine mycotic abortion.

Pathogens.
*Aspergillus flavus Link (Plum, 1932)
*A. fumigatus Fresen. (Bendixen & Plum, 1929)
*A. nidulans (Eidam) Wint. (Plum, 1932)
A. niger Van Tieghem, (Jungherr, 1935)
A. terreus Thom, (Plum, 1932)
A. versicolor (Vuill.) Tiraboschi (Plum, 1932)
*Allescheria boydii Shear (Rowsell, 1955)
Monotospora lanuginosa (Griff. & Maublanc) Mason (de Vries, 1955; personal communication)
*Absidia corymbifera (Cohn) Sacc. & Trot. (Plum, 1932)
*A. ramosa (Lindt) Lendner (Bendixen & Plum, 1929)
Mortierella polycephala ? (van Ulsen, 1955)
*Mucor pusillus Lindt (Jungherr, 1935)
Rhizopus arrhizus Fischer (Plum, 1932)
Syn. R. bovinus van Beyma (Plum, 1932)
*R. cohnii Berl. & Toni (Jungherr, 1935)
Syn. Mucor rhizopodiformis Cohn (T. Smith, 1920)
R. microsporus van Tieghem (Syn. R. equinus Cost. & Lucet (Ballarini, 1955))
*Nocardia asteroides Blanchard (Fey et al., 1954)
Candida tropicalis (Cast.) Berkhout (Austwick & Venn, 1957)
Polystictus versicolor Fr. (Austwick & Venn, 1957)

*pathogenic for experimental animals

Host. Cattle

Geographical Distribution.
North America and Europe.
U.S.A. (T. Smith, 1920), Canada (Rowsell, 1955); Denmark (Bendixen & Plum, 1929), Norway (Iversen & Rød, 1950), Germany (Weidlich, 1952), Great Britain (Ainsworth & Austwick, 1955a, b), Italy (Ballarini, 1955), Netherlands (Engel & Van der Maas, 1955), Portugal (Moreira-Jacob & van Uden, 1955).

The first record of a fungus isolated from bovine foetal membranes was of Mucor rhizopodiformis (Rhizopus cohnii) found growing in a gravid uterus by Theobald Smith (1920). Gilman & Birch (1925) recorded actual abortion and Bendixen & Plum (1929) published a monograph on the disease. Until recently very little attention was paid to these papers, but the work has now been amply confirmed and knowledge of the disease considerably extended. Of the 18 species of fungi so far reported in association with abortions only about half are at present recognized pathogens, but almost all are able to grow at 37°C. In every case of the condition the fungus has been the only significant organism to be isolated from the foetus or its membranes, often in pure culture, and no concurrent infection by Brucella abortus or Vibrio fetus has been reported.

Symptomatology. Present knowledge of mycotic abortion is limited to the foetus and its membranes, for no author has recorded any noticeable symptoms in the dam, either before or after the act of abortion. A tentative clinical diagnosis may be made on the appearance of the placenta and particularly the cotyledons, and also on the presence of skin lesions on the foetus. Bendixen & Plum (1929) described in detail the characters of the infected placenta, in which the cotyledons may retain much of their maternal portion and are greatly thickened, especially at the margins. Central necrosis is also a common feature. The intercaruncular areas sometimes have a leather-like consistency with discrete and confluent thickenings.

Weidlich (1952) first observed skin lesions on a foetus and isolated Aspergillus fumigatus from them, but according to Austwick & Venn (1957) they are probably an unusual feature, having been present on only two out of 43 infected foetuses. One of these foetuses was about seven months old and had discrete, raised areas on the skin of the back and head and the other, about 3–4 months old, had diffuse whitish and wrinkled areas on the skin of the flanks, the neck and the axillae.

Pathology. Direct microscopic examination of the cotyledons and intercaruncular areas by crush preparations reveals the presence of hyphae in the tissue. In the amniotic fluid and the foetal stomach contents groups of hyphae may be clearly visible to the naked eye as feathery clumps often mixed with plaque-like aggregations of squamous epithelial cells. Hyphae are also easily detected in the foetal skin lesions.

Histological examination of the affected cotyledons by Bendixen & Plum (1929) showed extensive hyperaemia and haemorrhage in early infections, with scattered infiltration of polymorphonuclear cells and eosinophiles. Later necrosis spread between the chorion and the placental tissue tending to cause their separation by the formation of an exudate rich in hyphae. In the thickened intercaruncular areas there was marked proliferation of the epithelium with loss of its surface layers. Foetal skin lesions have not been examined histologically.

Mycology. Fungi have been recovered from the placenta, the amniotic fluid, foetal stomach contents and foetal skin lesions. Very rarely have isolations been made from the other organs of the foetus; e.g. the lungs (Moreira-Jacob & van Uden, 1955). Austwick & Venn (1957) found that the best isolation method for foetal stomach contents was to smear them, using a glass spreader, on to a malt agar plate (containing 20 units of penicillin and 40 units of streptomycin per ml.) and to incubate at 37°C. Colonies frequently appeared within 24 hours depending on the species of fungus involved, and the plates were retained for one week.

Isolation from the placenta presents some difficulty, for this material has invariably been exposed to the air, and, more often than not, been dropped on the ground. In this way very heavy fungal contamination may complicate the interpretation of the cultural results, for most of the fungi associated with abortion are also present in the litter and air of cowsheds (Rolle & Kolb, 1954). Generally the appearance of a fungus within 24 hours from pieces of a placenta plated on to malt agar (prepared as above), will indicate infection, provided the fungus isolated has the same hyphal morphology as that already seen in the material on direct examination. From the stomach contents the fungal growth is usually pure but there may be high bacterial contamination in foetuses aborted more than 24 hours before culture.

The 18 species of fungi recovered from foetuses and placentas cannot all be described here for they differ widely in character. Seven of them are Phycomycetes, 9 Fungi Imperfecti (including one species of yeast and two imperfect states of known Ascomycetes), and one a Basidiomycete. The single Actinomycete (Nocardia asteroides) isolated by Fey et al. (1954) deserves special mention for it will not grow on malt agar as described but will appear on blood agar plates prepared for bacteriological examination. The chief fungus associated with mycotic abortion is Aspergillus fumigatus which has been reported from over 60% of the cases. Absidia ramosa and A. corymbifera are also frequent isolates but the remaining species are rarely reported.

In the foetal stomach contents and the placenta the hyphae of Aspergillus fumigatus are narrow, branching, septate and 1.5–3.0 micra wide. In culture the fruiting structures of this fungus appear as small bluish-green heads with the typical structure of an Aspergillus. The Absidia spp. have hyphae 2.5–7.5 micra wide, of a different appearance, being much branched, non-septate and irregular in outline with numerous swellings. The cultural appearance is also characteristic in its fluffy white growth and the pear-shaped sporangia containing large numbers of spores. The shape of the sporangia distinguishes them from many species of Mucor which have globose sporangia, but the non-septate hyphae are a mucoraceous feature. Yeasts appear as round, oval or elongated budding cells and in culture usually form bacteria-like colonies which are opaque and may produce abundant mycelium in the agar. Other species of fungi also produce characteristic hyphae in pathological material, but isolation is always required for final identification.

Pathogenicity for experimental animals has been established in the case of those species marked with an asterisk in the list of pathogens, but the remaining 10 species have not yet been tested. Gilman & Birch (1925) first injected a pregnant cow with the spores of a Mucor sp. and produced abortion; Bendixen & Plum (1929) made further attempts by intravenous inoculation and were successful in five out of six cases using Aspergillus fumigatus and Absidia ramosa, the abortions taking place 1–2 months after inoculation. The sixth cow of the series died from what appeared to be pulmonary aspergillosis six days after inoculation, but even in this animal there was evidence of the early stages of placental invasion. Experimental feeding of cultures of these two fungi was without result.

Serology. No serological techniques have yet been used in the diagnosis of the disease.

Epidemiology. The epidemiology of the infection is imperfectly understood, but there is every indication that infection is originally derived from the spores of fungi present in large numbers in "mouldy" hay, straw, and feeding stuffs and hence also in the air of cowsheds (Rolle & Kolb, 1954; Ainsworth & Austwick, 1955a, b). Support for this assumption is given by the winter rise in incidence of the disease, Ainsworth & Austwick (1955a) having stated that 75% of the cases reported during the A.R.C. Survey of Animal Mycoses occurred between November and May, which corresponds roughly to the time of hay feeding. van Ulsen (1955) also noted that the percentage of cases doubled after the wet summer of 1954 when conditions for haymaking were poor. Bendixen & Plum (1929) considered that infection was primarily pulmonary but only transient in the lungs, spreading haematogenously to the placenta. Jungherr (1935) also thought that infection was respiratory and metastasized to the uterus, rather than ascending the genital tract. Indeed there is no evidence that infection is by the latter route. Rollinson & Haq (1948) reported the isolation of Absidia corymbifera from the preputial washings of a bull and the cervical mucus of a cow it had served, and Ainsworth & Austwick (1955a) gave a list of mould species isolated from the same sites in cases of infertility. Neither paper indicated whether the isolates were derived from spores or from groups of hyphae; a distinction which would have helped to differentiate active growth in the organ concerned from mere contamination. Further work is required on the portal of entry of infection and on the level of spore intake which is likely to set up the condition in susceptible, pregnant cows (see also Mammalian Aspergillosis, p. 7).

Treatment. No clinical symptoms have been observed in the dam before or after abortion and no treatment has ever been given to affected animals. As far as known, cows which abort fungus-infected foetuses may calve normally on the next occasion, but this may not always be so (Venn, 1956; personal communication). At present the spontaneous "recovery" of the dam is assumed to follow the regeneration of the uterine wall.

If the 5% infection rate for aborted bovine foetuses reported by Plum (1932) and by Austwick & Venn (1957) is general in temperate countries, measures to reduce this type of abortion are urgently needed, but until subclinical infection of the cow can be detected and the epidemiology is elucidated, some control of the condition might be effected by exercising greater care in the feeding of mouldy hay to pregnant animals. Treatment of hay with fungicides during haymaking in order to reduce subsequent mould growth might also help (Kennedy & Schenk, 1954).

Chapter 13

MYCOTIC MASTITIS

(Yeasts, moulds, actinomycetes, colourless algae)

Mycotic mastitis has been associated with over 26 species of fungi in probably both primary and secondary roles and has generally followed antibiotic treatment of bacterial mastitis. Clinical symptoms are very variable and the detection and isolation of the fungus are necessary for diagnosis. Recovery is generally spontaneous but may take up to five months. No treatment has proved really effective. Infection by Cryptococcus neoformans is the most serious form of the disease.

Disease Name. Mycotic mastitis.

Pathogens.

Name of organism	First record	Experimental transmission	No. of cases recorded
Saccharomyces fragilis Jörgensen	Tucker, 1954	Redaelli, 1957b	5
Candida pelliculosa Redaelli	Galli, 1954	Redaelli, 1957b	9
Candida tropicalis (Cast.) Berkh.	Ainsworth & Austwick, 1955b	Redaelli, 1957b	4
Cryptococcus neoformans (Sanf.) Vuill.	Pounden et al., 1952	Redaelli, 1957b	183
Trichosporon ?granulosum (Kambayashi) Ota	Murphy & Drake, 1947	Murphy & Drake, 1947	10
Aspergillus ?fumigatus Fres.	Ainsworth & Austwick, 1955a	—	1
Nocardia asteroides (Eppinger) Blanchard	Sforza, 1946	Pier et al., 1958	10
Prototheca ?zopfii Krüger	Lerche, 1952	Lerche, 1952	1

Other isolates of uncertain status from mastitis cases are listed below, the figures given after each species indicating the number of individual cases on record:-

Hansenula anomala (Hansen) H. & P. Sydow, 1; H. angusta Wickerham, 1;

Pichia farinosa (Lindner) Hansen, 22; Sporobolomyces roseus Kluyver & v. Niel., 1; Candida albicans (Robin) Berkh., 3; C. catenulata Diddens & Lodder, 2; C. guilliermondii (Cast.) Langeron, 5; C. krusei (Cast.) Berkh., 9; C. mesenterica (Geiger) Diddens & Lodder, 1; C. mycoderma (Reess.) Lodder & Kreger van Rij, 1; C. pulcherrima (Lindner) Windisch, 1; C. rugosa (Anderson) Diddens & Lodder, 2; C. solani Lodder & Kreger van Rij, 2; C. zeylanoides (Cast.) Langeron & Guerra, 3; Torulopsis candida (Saito) Lodder, 5; T. famata (Harrison) Lodder & Kreger van Rij, 1; Geotrichum candidum Link, 3; Prototheca portoricensis Cif., Ashf. & Dalmau, 1; various identified moulds were mentioned by Ainsworth & Austwick (1955a), and many unidentified yeasts and actinomycetes have been found by other authors.

References from which this list was compiled and which are not included above or in the text are:-

Benito-Trujillo et al., 1955; Blank, 1957b; Kauker, 1955; Munch-Petersen, 1954; Seele & Lauer, 1955; Smith, 1934.

Hosts. Cattle; goat.

Geographical distribution. Europe and North America.

Although bacteria are the predominant cause of bovine mastitis, single cases and occasional outbreaks of the disease have been attributed to infection by fungi. Only a few of these have been substantiated by the experimental reproduction of the disease with the suspected causal organism, but it is most likely that a number of the species of fungi regularly isolated from mastitis milk samples and at present considered to be without pathogenic significance, will eventually be shown to infect the bovine udder under certain conditions.

Apart from the almost prophetic suggestion by Thom (1928) that in certain cases the fungi found in milk might have come from udders with mycotic disease, the first reference to fungi as the cause of mastitis was by Rolle (1934), who isolated yeasts from five cows being fed on brewery by-products. There is little doubt that mycotic mastitis existed before the advent of antibacterial antibiotics, but since then there has been an increasing number of cases reported almost invariably associated with prior antibiotic treatment of diagnosed or suspected bacterial mastitis.

From a study of the literature it has not always been easy to relate the fungi which have appeared in cultures of mastitis milk to their actual presence in the affected udder and it is probable that a number of isolates were contaminants derived from the cowshed air, the teat surfaces, or the collecting vessel. Possibly the copious growth in milk of Geotrichum candidum (Syn. Oidium lactis) reported by early workers, the presence of Saccharomyces exiguus found in normal milk by Zürn (1877) and the 17 species of filamentous fungi listed by Ainsworth & Austwick (1954), were all contaminants. It is the yeasts and actinomycetes which seem to be best adapted to growth in the ducts and acini of the udder, by virtue of their ability to break up into small vegetatively-reproducing units, thus closely resembling the bacterial method of growth. From the point of view of rapid spread and penetration filamentous fungi are at a disadvantage when growing in a liquid medium if compared with the yeasts and the only certain case of mastitis due to a mould, is that briefly reported by Ainsworth & Austwick (1955a) in which a fungus, thought to be Aspergillus fumigatus, was present in a large mycetoma in the udder of a goat.

One of the more unsatisfactory aspects of the disease is the lack of specific determination of the isolated fungi, for only 10 of the 20 accounts of mycotic udder infection give the name of the fungus involved. Few data on the relative importance of the different species are available, but reference to the list of species and the numbers of cases reported for each, shows that some species occur much more frequently than others. A start on the experimental production of the disease with known fungi has been made by Redaelli (1957a, b) and these papers should provide very useful information for pathogenicity studies.

With so few background data, mycotic mastitis is not a commonly recognized disease but there is some evidence that it might be more frequently reported if mycological examination of mastitis milk was undertaken instead of relying on normal bacteriological cultural and staining techniques. The species of fungi so far isolated from mastitis milk show a wide range of types with a predominance of yeasts. So far there are on record some 430 individual cases of mycotic mastitis of which over half occurred in 13 outbreaks, one involving 106 cows. One of the few estimates of incidence in a herd has been made by Burkey et al. (1951), who recorded 64 cases during 1945–50 with the yearly incidence varying from none to 8% of all cases of mastitis.

Symptomatology. At present there is no evidence that mycotic mastitis is clinically distinguishable from the bacterial disease, but further study may reveal criteria which might be used for a tentative diagnosis. Cryptococcal mastitis (Cryptococcus neoformans infection) is by far the most serious type and it has already been mentioned under cryptococcosis. Pounden et al. (1952) found that the symptoms were most variable, but a number of cows showed a characteristic gradual development over a period of several days of severe swelling in more than one quarter which persisted for a long time. In the outbreak described by Simon et al. (1953) loss of appetite and a rise in temperature were noted, but the absence of toxaemia was a feature. Galli (1954), on the other hand, reported that swelling occurred in all four quarters within 12 hours of the administration of penicillin for the treatment of streptococcal mastitis, and was accompanied by cessation of milk production, subcutaneous oedema of the udder, perineum and sternum, and swelling of the supramammary and internal iliac lymph nodes, but no rise in temperature. In all cases the drop in milk yield was dramatic and in many cows, permanent.

In the cases associated with other yeasts, the symptoms appear to have been much milder (Galli, 1954), with the acute phase of the disease characteristically occurring 2–3 days after antibiotic treatment of bacterial mastitis and being followed by a gradual recovery over a comparatively long period of up to five months (Hulse, 1952), during which time yeast cells may still be detected in the milk. The nature of the secretion varies in the different stages of the disease but greyish or yellowish floccules have been reported (Andersen & Jørgensen, 1949) and the cryptococcal infection may produce a mucilaginous secretion.

Pathology. Yeast cells and actinomycete filaments can be detected in wet preparations of the udder secretion, but are not always easy to distinguish from the other bodies in milk. Smears stained with the periodic acid-Schiff technique are probably the most satisfactory for distinguishing yeast cells but actinomycete filaments require Gram staining or an acid-fast technique for differentiation.

It is most probable that a characteristic tissue response to fungal infection occurs with a well-defined cellular reaction with polymorphonuclear cells, eosinophiles and histiocytes predominating together with epithelial cells. The histopathology of the udder lesions has been investigated only in cases of cryptococcal mastitis. In these Innes et al. (1952) described the changes from the acute to the chronic stage which ended in the destruction of all except the fibrous framework of the gland. Galli (1954) found granulomatous foci up to the size of a pea in the udder tissue.

Mycology. The isolation of yeasts and filamentous fungi from milk is normally accomplished without difficulty by using malt or Sabouraud's glucose agar preferably with added antibacterial antibiotics. Incubation should normally be carried out at 37° and 25°C. Aerobic actinomycetes may be isolated on blood or nutrient agar at 37°C. but will not grow in the presence of the antibiotics.

The filamentous fungi, e.g. Aspergillus fumigatus, may be recognized by their morphology on direct examination but almost all yeast species require extensive study of their morphological and physiological characters before they can be identified. Reference to this problem has already been made under moniliasis, and it must be stressed here that the identity of the species involved in the case or outbreak is of great importance. The monograph of Lodder & Kreger van Rij (1952) has greatly facilitated the identification of yeasts, but at present these fungi are still a specialized field of mycology.

Cryptococcus neoformans is undoubtedly the most important yeast causing mastitis, and its early detection is essential if a severe outbreak involving the slaughter of affected animals is to be prevented. Fortunately it is rare but the outbreaks already referred to are evidence of its virulence. It may be detected in the udder secretion by its large cells, 5–20 micra in diameter, each surrounded by a wide, transparent mucilaginous capsule. Colonies on malt agar are cream or buff coloured and usually extremely slimy, characters shared by some of the saprophytic Cryptococcus spp., so that final identification must rest on the physiological tests and intracerebral inoculation of mice.

Of the other commonly isolated yeasts, Pichia farinosa is one of the more frequent (Lernau et al., 1947). It forms a white, powdery-surfaced colony on malt agar, and its elongated cells fuse (conjugate) in unequal pairs (anisogamously) to form 4-spored asci. Saccharomyces fragilis forms a smooth, greyish-brown, matt, creeping colony on malt agar, has narrow elongated cells, bean-shaped ascospores, and closely resembles Candida krusei which is considered to be its imperfect (non-ascosporic) state. In the genus Trichosporon, the hyphae split up into arthrospores as well as forming normal budding yeast cells. It may be noted that Candida albicans, so often involved in human and avian infections, has been found associated with mastitis on three occasions only, and has in fact rarely been isolated from cattle, van Uden & do Carmo Sousa (1957) having failed to find it among 131 yeast isolates obtained from 252 bovine caeca. These authors considered that it was replaced by C. tropicalis as a common alimentary commensal and it is not surprising that the latter species figures as a moderately frequent cause of mastitis (see Šipka, 1957).

The characters of Nocardia asteroides have already been described under nocardiosis, and descriptions of several of the filamentous fungi isolated from milk will be found under aspergillosis and mucormycosis. The colourless pathogenic alga Prototheca greatly resembles a yeast both in its cultural appearance and its morphology, but instead of budding it forms four or more vegetative spores inside each of the large oblong cells (6–16 x 5–11 micra) and these are freed by the rupture of the parent cell wall into two equal parts. It is not clear at present whether the two species isolated from mastitis cases, P. zopfii and P. portoricensis, are identical but the pathogenicity of the former for the bovine udder has been shown by Lerche (1952).

Epidemiology. The use of antibiotics as the standard treatment for bovine mastitis makes the evaluation of fungi as a primary cause of the disease extremely difficult. Whenever details are available it appears that fungal infection has almost always followed antibiotic therapy, occasionally without any evidence that bacteria were primarily involved. Among the preceding bacterial infections reported have been those caused by Corynebacterium pyogenes, Escherichia coli, Serratia indica, Staphylococcus aureus, Streptococcus agalactiae, Str. faecalis, and Str. uberis, and it is therefore probable that in many cases the fungi are secondary invaders colonizing the necrotic material left after the elimination of the bacteria. This may be the reason why Redaelli (1957a, b) found that he could set up primary mastitis in cows and goats with only four species of yeast; possibly five other species frequently reported from mastitis cases can establish infection only in already damaged tissue.

The source of the fungi, particularly of the yeasts, associated with mastitis is virtually unknown, for knowledge of their natural occurrence is very scanty. The normal yeast floras of plant and animal substrates and that in the air are just becoming known and the only material linked with the occurrence of mycotic mastitis has been "brewers grains" — the soaked remains of the malted barley after the wort has been drained off. These "grains" have a high feeding value and although initially without a yeast flora, they appear to be an excellent substrate for yeast growth and most probably become quickly contaminated. Because only the wort is inoculated with brewers' yeast, "brewers' grains" never come in contact with this species (Saccharomyces cerevisiae) and in fact it has never been reported from an udder infection. At least six outbreaks have been associated with the feeding of brewers' grains, but unfortunately in no case was the causal organism identified. Airborne yeasts are predominantly non-fermentative (di Menna, 1955b) and rarely seem to be involved, but many of the filamentous fungi are known to be abundant as spores in the air of cowsheds. Sometimes the infecting fungus is in therapeutic material or its diluent, for Andersen & Jørgensen (1949) found that the distilled water used to dilute the stock penicillin solution contained a similar yeast to that isolated from the mastitis cases.

Perhaps the most significant finding in relation to the epidemiology of mycotic mastitis has been the discovery by Emmons (1955c) that a high proportion of the pigeon droppings he collected in barns contained Cryptococcus neoformans, although this fungus does not appear to cause any disease in the birds themselves. Dust from pigeon lofts, barn rafters or soil (Emmons, 1951) may thus have been the source of infection in the extensive outbreaks of cryptococcal mastitis already referred to. In each case the disease had followed antibiotic treatment.

Another factor concerning the epidemiology of the condition is the frequent occurrence of yeasts which form a pellicle in liquids. Surface films of these yeasts would tend to cling to dairy utensils and, under conditions of inadequate sterilization, could be transferred to the hands of the milkers and so to the udders of the cows. Contamination of dry-stored teat cups by a Candida sp. was reported recently by Simon & Hall (1955) during an investigation of an outbreak of mastitis apparently caused by the same fungus.

Treatment. With the exception of the cryptococcal infection, mycotic mastitis appears to be a self-limiting disease with an acute phase subsiding in most cases within a few days. A delay of two days in diagnosis is therefore often sufficient to allow for spontaneous recovery so that reports of successful treatment are very difficult to assess. Such treatments as have been used have been directed more towards the alleviation of the symptoms than to the control of the pathogen involved. Thus Galli (1954) treated nine cases of Candida pelliculosa infection by stripping out 3–4 times a day and found an improvement in a few days. Steele-Bodger (1953), dealing with 17 cases associated with unspecified yeasts, injected the infected quarters with an iodine and liquid paraffin preparation and claimed to have obtained improvement within 24 hours. Tucker (1954) tried cold applications and stimulants. Mastitis due to Nocardia asteroides (Sforza, 1946) and other aerobic actinomycetes would appear to respond to the normal therapy for bacterial mastitis as these organisms are mostly susceptible to the commonly used antibiotics.

Cryptococcal mastitis presents a much more serious problem in control because of the severe losses it may entail and the possible danger to man from contact with infective material, although there is no record of such transmission. In the outbreak described by Pounden et al. (1952), 23 compounds were tested in vitro against the fungus, but the few which proved active failed to show any real effect in vivo. With the same type of infection, Ségretain et al. (1956) found that cycloheximide at a daily dosage of 24 mg. per quarter for nine days was well tolerated and apparently led to improvement in the condition.

Normal hygienic measures including the segregation of affected cows and the careful sterilization of dairy utensils appear to provide the best method of controlling outbreaks in the absence of any really effective udder treatment. The immediate cessation of antibacterial antibiotic treatment when this has proved ineffective, seems to be an important step, for enhancement of the pathogenicity of Candida albicans has been noted in mice and chick embryos treated with aureomycin and penicillin respectively (Seligmann, 1952; Foley & Winter, 1949), and it is possible that similar factors may operate in the bovine udder. A close watch should also be kept on the microflora of the secretion for the reappearance of pathogenic bacteria and for the gradual decrease in yeast cells.

Wilson (1957) considers that where bacterial mastitis has occurred there is no difference between the susceptibility of infected and uninfected quarters to subsequent yeast infection, and that recrudescence of mycotic infection in the same quarter is uncommon. Moreover once the initial phase is over the infection shows little tendency to spread to other cows.

Experimental inoculation. Rolle (1934) tried inoculating the udder of a normal cow with the yeast he isolated from a mastitis case and produced swelling within 24 hours which persisted for more than ten days, whilst yeast cells could be recovered from the milk for a month afterwards. Using Prototheca zopfii, Lerche (1952) found that a swelling occurred after eight days and that cells persisted in the milk for up to five months. In Hulse's (1952) experiments recovery took eight weeks after the inoculation of 300 million yeast cells into the teat canal, whilst Stuart (1951) reproduced the condition in two out of seven quarters only by infusion of secretion from infected udders, the incubation period being 16 hours in one and 3 days in the other. Up to 60 million cells of the isolate grown in pure culture failed to set up the disease.

In the most recent series of experimental inoculations, Redaelli (1957a, b) found that with Candida tropicalis, C. pelliculosa, and Saccharomyces fragilis reaction occurred in 1–6 days according to the number of cells injected and each species produced a different pathological response. With Cryptococcus neoformans symptoms did not appear until 16–36 days after inoculation. He failed to produce infection with Hansenula anomala, Pichia farinosa, Candida albicans, C. krusei and C. solani.

Chapter 14

DISEASES CAUSED BY ACTINOMYCETES

'One of the most remarkable facts about Actinomycosis is the volume of literature which has been written about it, and the small amount of information contained therein' (Henrici, 1930). This statement is unfortunately still true in spite of notable investigations during the past twenty years which have thrown much light on both the aetiology and epidemiology of diseases caused by actinomycetes. Among the important contributory factors to this unsatisfactory state of affairs are, or have been, first, the practice of diagnosing actinomycosis by the presence of granules (the so-called 'sulphur granules') in the exudate from lesions or in infected tissue, without appreciating that these bodies are not produced solely by actinomycetes; and secondly the difficulty of isolating and culturing certain actinomycetes, which has led to much uncertainty regarding the identity of the pathogens involved. In order to set modern views in perspective the historical background will first be indicated by briefly summarizing facts which should now be familiar.

Actinomycosis was first recognized in cattle by Bollinger in 1877 and it was his botanical colleague Harz who introduced the name Actinomyces in the binomial Actinomyces bovis. These workers had before them both 'lumpy jaw' (caused by an actinomycete) and 'actinobacillosis' ('wooden tongue') caused by Actinobacillus lignieresi Brumpt, a bacterium able to form granules. Like many subsequent workers they did not distinguish between the two conditions which have since been confused with 'botryomycosis' of cattle and horses caused by another granule-forming bacterium which is very closely related to, if not identical with, Staphylococcus pyogenes. 'Actinomycosis' has thus been applied to a variety of pathological conditions although by microscopic examination only the true actinomycete granule is seen to be composed not of bacterial cells as in actinobacillosis and botryomycosis but of fine interwoven filaments.

Bollinger and Harz did not isolate the pathogens, but Bostroem in 1890 obtained from both bovine and human sources an aerobic actinomycete which he considered to be the causal organism, and in the following year Israel isolated an anaerobic actinomycete from actinomycosis in man. Bostroem's organism (the Actinomyces graminis of Topley & Wilson) proved to be identical with forms found outside the human body in grass and other vegetable matter and non-pathogenic to experimental animals, and there is now general agreement that the anaerobic organism described by Israel and which is known only from animal sources is responsible for classical actinomycosis. Unfortunately, both aerobic and anaerobic actinomycetes were classified in the genus Actinomyces until 1943, when Waksman and Henrici made taxonomic proposals which have since been adopted in the current edition of Bergey's Manual of determinative bacteriology and approved by bacteriologists and mycologists throughout the world. Waksman & Henrici's (1943) proposals included the reservation of Actinomyces for anaerobic forms and the distribution of aerobic actinomycetes in the genus Nocardia and in a new genus which they designated Streptomyces. In this review the term actinomycosis is, in line with current usage, reserved for disease resulting from infection by anaerobic actinomycetes of the Actinomyces 'bovis-israeli' type while diseases caused by aerobic forms are dealt with under nocardiosis.

ACTINOMYCOSIS
(Actinomyces bovis, A. israeli)

A chronic, granulomatous infection of cattle and other animals, caused by anaerobic actinomycetes, which is suspected when 'granules' are present in exudates or infected tissues. The diagnosis must be confirmed by microscopic examination of the granules and by culturing the pathogen. Actinomycosis responds to penicillin therapy.

Disease Name. Actinomycosis. Syn. Lumpy jaw (especially of cattle).

Pathogens. Anaerobic actinomycetes of the Actinomyces bovis Harz, 1877 — A. israeli (Kruse) Lachner-Sandoval, 1891 group. For synonymy see Bergey's Manual of determinative bacteriology, Ed. 6, 1948, p. 925 (A. bovis), p. 926 (A. israeli).

Hosts. Cattle, horse, pig, sheep, dog, cat; deer (Ryff, 1953); ferret (Collet et al., 1952); Isthmian capybara (Calero & Ortiz, 1947).
Also man, see Conant et al. (1954), pp. 1–25.

Geographical distribution. World-wide in both animals and man.

Symptomatology. The classical expression of actinomycosis in animals is bovine 'lumpy jaw' in which there is bone involvement, particularly of the lower jaw. A good account of this condition, which has been described many times, is that by Mohler & Shahan (1943). Other sites may be affected in cattle including the digestive tract (Bruere, 1955), the omentum (Beaver, 1921), heart (Fava & Zanacca, 1951), kidney (Awrorow, 1932), eye (Pelouro, 1943), udder (Hardenbrook, 1946; Smith, 1934), and testis (Bieberdorf, 1953; Kimball et al., 1954). In man a similar wide range of organs is attacked (see Cope, 1938) but infection of the jaw is relatively rare.

In sheep, actinomycosis is similar to that in cattle but there is frequently a chronic nodular bronchopneumonia, according to Lesbouyries (1952), while in the pig, in which the udder is frequently affected (Magnusson, 1928), pulmonary actinomycosis has also been recorded by Vawter (1946). Roderick at al. (1948) recorded the isolation of A. bovis (often in association with Brucella) from a large number of cases of fistulous withers and poll evil of horses in the U.S.A. and Burns & Simmons (1952) tentatively identified A. bovis from a swollen and fibrosed mandibular lymph node in the horse.

Because of confusion with infections caused by aerobic actinomycetes there is uncertainty regarding many of the records of canine actinomycosis. Menges et al., (1953) recorded two definite cases of A. bovis infections in dogs, of the lungs and omentum, respectively, and summarized the earlier literature. Among the smaller number of records of actinomycosis in cats the one by Edington (1934) may be mentioned.

Pathology. More has been written about the pathology of actinomycosis in man (see Cope, 1938; Conant et al., 1954) than in animals, but in all hosts the most characteristic feature, and one which allows a tentative diagnosis of actinomycosis to be made, is the 'granules' (often referred to as 'sulphur granules' because of their yellowish colour) which develop in infected tissues and which escape in the discharge from abscesses. Granule formation is not diagnostic for actinomycetes and in bovine infections there has been much confusion between actinobacillosis caused by Actinobacillus lignieresi and actinomycosis. (Mangrulkar (1938) may be consulted for an interesting discussion of this confusion.) Actinobacillosis (or 'wooden tongue') usually attacks the softer tissues of the mouth (in actinomycosis there is frequently bone involvement) and the granule on microscopic examination is seen to be composed of rod-like elements and not of fine filaments as in an actinomycete granule. In sections, the tips of the hyphae round the edge of an actinomycete granule are seen to be characteristically swollen, the so-called 'clubs', and they stain differentially with eosin. Clubs, which are probably an expression of a host-parasite interaction, are not invariably present and sometimes granule formation is absent.

Mycology. A tentative diagnosis of actinomycosis is made by demonstrating that the 'granules' associated with the lesions are composed of delicate, branching, Gram-positive hyphae approximately 1 micron in diameter or by observing short, Gram-positive hyphal fragments in pus or other exudate, but without making cultures it is impossible to distinguish with certainty anaerobic from aerobic actinomycetes. The anaerobic forms have rather specialized growth requirements (see Erikson & Porteous, 1953) and are difficult to maintain in culture. Isolations may, however, be made by inoculating brain–heart–glucose broth (or agar) and incubating at 37° C. in an atmosphere of nitrogen, when growth develops in 4–7 days. Erikson & Porteous (1953), from a study of the nutritional requirements of Actinomyces israeli, recommended a heart broth–casein digest medium, on which they were able to maintain several strains for prolonged periods by making weekly transfers to fresh medium.

Opinions regarding the status of the organisms causing classical actinomycosis differ and the present situation may be briefly summarized as follows. Erikson (1940), in England, made a detailed study of anaerobic actinomycetes from both human and bovine cases of actinomycosis and found certain differences between strains from the two sources. The outstanding differences were: 'morphologically, a greater degree of polymorphism on the part of the human strains and, in particular, a firm, generally adherent growth on solid media, whereas the bovine strains form more uniform, soft, smooth, colonies; physiologically, a greater ability to ferment sugars on the part of the human strains; serologically, a lack of reaction between the two types'. She regarded the human and bovine strains as distinct species which she designated 'A. israeli Kruse' and 'A. bovis Harz', respectively. Erikson was followed in the Sixth Edition of Bergey's Manual of determinative bacteriology, 1948, where A. israeli (Kruse) Lachner-Sandoval is distinguished from A. bovis Harz, a distinction which was maintained by Thompson (1950) in the U.S.A. from a comparative study of 8 human and 11 bovine strains. This viewpoint has not, however, been unanimously accepted. Conant et al. (1954), in line with the prevailing opinion in the U.S.A., consider human and bovine actinomycosis to be caused by one organism which they designate A. bovis, while Prévot (1953) in France distinguished from human and animal sources a number of species of pathogenic anaerobic actinomycetes which he classified in the genus Actinobacterium.

Recently, there has been a further complication. It had for long been noted that in the animal host pathogenic actinomycetes are accompanied by other micro-organisms (e.g. Actinobacillus actinomycetemcomitans (Klinger) Topley & Wilson, see Bergey's Manual, Ed. 6, 1948, p. 557) and Erikson & Porteous (1955) have recorded the conversion of a 'rough' typical strain of Actinomyces israeli of human origin to a 'smooth', soft form more tolerant of oxygen by the physical trapping within the mycelium of a few alien and facultative aerobic cells which, when isolated by micromanipulation, commonly proved to be staphylococci, a result which, while not disproving the specific identity of A. bovis in the sense of Bergey's Manual, suggests that some at least of the records of soft, smooth anaerobic actinomycetes are of commensal associations of A. israeli with other organisms. For the time being it would seem best to retain A. israeli and A. bovis for the 'rough' and 'smooth' forms in the sense of Bergey's Manual in spite of the additional fact that the binomial A. bovis is, for various technical reasons, of doubtful validity under the International Code of Bacteriological Nomenclature. In many records of actinomycosis in both man and animals, the identity of the pathogen cannot be definitely verified because of the taxonomic uncertainties. As already inferred, Erikson (1940) and Thompson (1950) have recorded A. israeli from man and A. bovis from cattle. One of Thompson's (1950) bovine isolates was of the A. israeli type and Erikson & Porteous (1955) also recorded A. israeli from cattle and pigs. Among other definite records are A. bovis from a deer (Ryff, 1953) and dogs (Menges et al., 1953) and from horses (Kimball & Frank, 1945). Prévot (1953) ascribed canine and feline cases of actinomycosis to Actinobacterium baudeti.

Experimental actinomycosis. Many workers have reported difficulty in establishing actinomycosis in experimental animals. Hazen et al. (1952) recommended 3- to 4-week-old male hamsters as the experimental animal of choice while progressive actinomycosis in young albino mice has been increased from 31.9 to 94.6% by mixing the A. bovis inoculum with gastric mucin (Meyer & Verges, 1950). Both groups of workers employed intraperitoneal inoculation.

Serology. Erikson (1940) detected antigenic differences between the human and bovine strains which she studied. Earlier, Magnusson (1928) had differentiated three serological types of A. bovis; type A being characteristic of cattle, types B and C of swine infections, and subsequently Slack et al. (1955) found twenty isolates of anaerobic actinomycetes from man and cattle to fall into two serological groups which showed no correlation with the habitat. The taxonomic implications of these findings are not yet clear.

The host is sensitized, but the degree of sensitization in man appears too variable to allow its use as a diagnostic aid and the same probably applies to natural infections in animals. In human cases successful cures have been reported by the use of vaccines, in spite of the fact that the vaccines have sometimes been prepared from aerobic species.

Epidemiology. Traditionally, human actinomycosis has been considered to have an exogenous origin, and works of reference still commonly state or imply that infection occurs as a result of chewing infected straw, grass etc. The incidence of actinomycosis is certainly higher in rural than in urban populations (Porter, 1953), but the pathogen does not appear ever to have been isolated from vegetable material or from soil, which, however, yield an abundance of aerobic actinomycetes. The evidence seems rather to point to actinomycosis being endogenous, for though its distribution is world wide, no exogenous source of infection has been demonstrated. A. israeli is frequently harboured in the tonsillar crypts and found in association with carious teeth of apparently healthy individuals and has the exacting nutritional requirements suggestive of a well-adapted parasite. The role of vegetable matter is, as suggested by Cope (1938), probably limited to causing slight injuries by which the pathogen gains access to deeper tissues. For animals too an endogenous origin seems most likely. The evidence is similar to that for human actinomycosis, but there have been fewer records of the association of anaerobic actinomycetes with apparently normal animals — perhaps because fewer attempts at isolation have been made. Davis (1923) found A. bovis in the tonsillar crypts of pigs but not of cattle, while Frost (1940) recorded organisms of the A. bovis group from the mouths of normal cattle.

Therapy. The prognosis for cases of human actinomycosis was grave before the introduction of penicillin to which the disease readily responds. Similar success has been obtained by the penicillin treatment of bovine cases (Lewis, 1947). Kingman & Palen (1951) have also claimed successful results with streptomycin. Before the introduction of antibiotics, intravenous injection of sodium iodide was the standard treatment (Farquarson, 1937; Pullar, 1939) and for man iodide is advocated as a supplement to any other treatment. Dicke (1953) checked a mandibular infection in a bull by inoculation of the site with blowfly maggots and Ansbacher (1954) recorded the successful treatment of a bovine case with isoniazid ("Nydrazid").

NOCARDIOSIS

(Syn. Actinomycosis and Streptothricosis in part)

It is impossible from a survey of the literature to give a critical integrated account of nocardiosis in animals caused by species of Nocardia because of uncertainties regarding the identity of the pathogen in many cases and because of inadequate descriptions of the clinical findings. Clarification can result only from extensive investigation of new cases in the light of studies of cultures and other evidence available from the better documented of the earlier records. Here, various records of species of Nocardia pathogenic for animals are listed and annotated under hosts. Literature references already compiled in Bergey's Manual of determinative bacteriology, 6th Edit. (1948) and in Dodge's Medical Mycology (Dodge, 1935) have not usually been cited again.

The genus Nocardia differs from Actinomyces in that some of its species are obligately aerobic and others microaerophilic, and by the partially acid-fast staining qualities of the hyphae. Spores are produced, as in Actinomyces, by the breaking-up of the hyphae into arthrospores and not, as in the aerobic Streptomyces, on special aerial branches (conidiophores).

Dog.

Nocardia asteroides (Eppinger) Blanchard, 1895. (Bergey's Manual, 1948, p. 896; Dodge (1935, p. 750.)

N. asteroides is one of the best-known aerobic actinomycetes pathogenic for man (see Conant et al. (1954), pp. 26–45) and there are a number of records from various parts of the world of canine nocardiosis caused by this species (Schwabe, 1954). The symptoms do not appear to be diagnostic and canine nocardiosis is recognized with difficulty. In the first American case reported by Bohl et al. (1953) there was a sublaryngeal swelling which on post-mortem examination was found to extend from a large superficial ulcer in the perilaryngeal and tracheal tissue as well as into the parotid salivary gland. The bronchial lymph nodes were also infected. Smears from various parts of the lesion revealed Gram-positive, actinomycete filaments, and cultures yielded a partially acid-fast actinomycete which corresponded with N. asteroides. The first record of N. asteroides from the dog was that by Balozet & Pernot (1936) from France, and other records have been made by Ginsberg & Little (1948), from Scotland; Cross et al. (1953), Hawaii; Pillai (1953), Ceylon; Cilli et al. (1954), Eritrea; Blake (1954), Missouri; Fey et al. (1954), Denmark; and in the Annual Report of the Senior Research Officer, Sudan Veterinary Service, 1942, p. 24.

Actinomyces canis (Rabe) Gasperini, 1894. (Bergey's Manual, 1948, p. 915; Dodge (1935), p. 748.)

Canestrelli (1939), Italy; Gray & Hoeben (1941), Australia; Pallaske (1952), Germany. Cedervall (1954) recorded this species (as Streptothrix canis) from dogs, cats, otters, a silver fox and a mink in Sweden.

Nocardia bicolor (Trolldenier) de Mello & Fernandes, 1919. (Bergey's Manual, 1948, p. 919; Dodge (1935), p. 748.)

Associated with cerebro-meningitis, bronchitis and lymphadenitis; Germany.

Streptomyces galtieri Goret & Joubert (1951).

From a case of generalized actinomycosis in a dog; France.

Cat.

Actinomyces canis, see under Dog.

Cattle.

Nocardia farcinica Trevisan, 1889. (Bergey's Manual, 1948, p. 895; Dodge (1935), p. 746.

Cattle farcy or lymphangitis. Reported from Guadeloupe, Sumatra, India, Ceylon (where it is known as "kora gedi" – the boil which lames), Kenya, Somaliland and the Republic of the Sudan. The disease is characterized by gross enlargement of the subcutaneous lymph nodes, especially the prescapular and popliteal, followed by ulceration of the tumour-like swellings. Lung involvement has occasionally been reported (Curasson, 1942). There is little agreement on the nature of the causal organism of bovine farcy. Nocard (1888) originally described an aerobic actinomycete from the Guadeloupe material and Holmes (1908) made similar isolations in India. Vrÿburg (1908), in Sumatra, and Raymond (1910), who investigated the same outbreak as Holmes, both considered that a small bacillus was the causal agent. Sheather (1920) agreed with this observation, but Daubney (1927) was convinced that he had isolated Nocardia farcinica. Other workers have failed to recover any organism in culture (Castellani & Sturgess, 1905). It therefore seems that there are either at least two different organisms causing the disease or one or both of these forms are contaminants and not the aetiological agents. Cattle farcy is clearly in urgent need of re-investigation to establish conclusively the nature of the causal organism. The chronic form of "lumpy skin" disease of cattle (Henning, 1956) has many points of resemblance to cattle farcy.

Nocardia asteroides (Eppinger) Blanchard, 1895. (See under Dog.)

Cow (lungs), U. S. A. (Bishop & Fenstermacher, 1933); (udder), Australia (Munch-Petersen, 1954); (associated with abortion), Denmark (Fey et al., 1954).

Nocardia pulmonalis (Burnett) Bergey et al., 1948. (Bergey's Manual, 1948, p. 901.)

Cow (lungs), U. S. A.

Nocardia valvulae Chalmers & Christopherson, 1916. (Bergey's Manual, 1948, p. 922; Dodge (1935), p. 757.)

Endocarditis, Germany.

Actinomyces actinoides (Th. Smith) Bergey et al., 1923. (Dodge (1935), p. 716.)

Calves (pneumonia), U. S. A.

Actinomyces spitzi (Lignières & Spitz) Dodge, 1935. (Dodge (1935), p.752.)
Oxen (upper jaw), Argentina.

Horse.

Nocardia equi Chalmers & Christopherson, 1916. (Bergey's Manual, 1948, p. 920; Dodge (1935), p. 758.)
Nodule on jaw.

Nocardia polychromogenes (Vallée) Bergey et al., 1948. (Bergey's Manual, 1948, p. 897; Dodge (1935), p. 737.)
Blood of horse dead from Pasteurella infection.

Nocardia blackwellii (Erikson) Bergey et al., 1948. (Bergey's Manual, 1948, p. 910; Erikson (1935), pp. 32, 37.)
Hock joint of a foal.

Goat.

Nocardia caprae (Silberschmidt) Bergey et al., 1948. (Bergey's Manual, 1948, p. 899; Dodge (1935), p. 748.)
Goat (lung), Switzerland.

Fowls.

Actinomyces tossicus (Rossi) Dodge, 1935. (Bergey's Manual, 1948, p. 918; Dodge (1935), p. 719.)
Tumours in the abdominal cavity, Italy.

Nocardia dassonvillei (Brocq-Rousseu) Liégard & Landrieu, 1911. (Bergey's Manual, 1948, p. 915.)
Liver (Truche, 1926).

Marsupials.

Nocardia macrodipodidarum Fox, 1923. (Bergey's Manual, 1948, p. 921; Dodge (1935), p. 747.)
A disease somewhat similar to lumpy jaw, affecting marsupials in zoological gardens: Fox (1923), U. S. A.; Scott (1925), wallabies, London zoo; Beveridge (1934); Tucker & Millar (1953), Brisbane, Australia.

Camel.

Actinomyces cameli (Mason) Sartory & Bailly, 1923. (Bergey's Manual, 1948, p. 915; Sartory (1923), p. 822.)
From pseudotuberculous lesions.

Rabbit.

Nocardia cuniculi Snijders, 1924. (Bergey's Manual, 1948, p.910; Dodge (1935), p. 712; Erikson (1935), p. 32.)

Rat.

Actinomyces salvati Langeron, 1922. (Bergey's Manual, 1948, p. 917.)

Nocardia sanfelicei Redaelli, 1928. (Bergey's Manual, 1948, p. 921; Dodge (1935), p. 751.)

Guinea-pig.

Nocardia caviae Snijders, 1924. (Bergey's Manual, 1948, p.912; Erikson (1935), p. 32.

Disorders associated with other aerobic Actinomycetes

Horse.

Nocardia chalmersi de Mello & Fernandes, 1919. (Bergey's Manual, 1948, p. 975; Dodge (1935), p. 734.)
From saliva.

Actinomyces caballus Morquer & Comby (1942).
Subcutaneous abscess, France.

Cat.

Actinomyces cati (Rivolta) Gasperini, 1894. (Bergey's Manual, 1948, p. 969.

Turkey.

Streptothrix sp. (? Streptomyces sp.).
Skin infection, associated with Candida albicans, England (Soliman & Rollinson, 1951).

Respiratory disorders associated with Streptomyces species

The association of Streptomyces spp. with unexplained respiratory trouble during winter in calves and piglets was first reported by Ainsworth & Austwick (1955a). From material and cultures sent in for examination, Streptomyces spp. of the albus series were obtained in quantity on 25 occasions from the lungs of animals dying shortly after the onset of general weakness, diarrhoea and respiratory distress. From 13 of these, no other organisms were isolated, but associated fungi in the remaining cases included Aspergillus fumigatus, A. nidulans, A. terreus, Absidia ramosa and A. corymbifera. Histological examination failed to reveal the presence of the organisms in recognizable form in the lungs and it seemed possible that an allergic response was involved. On several occasions very large quantities of Streptomyces-like spores were found in samples of the poor quality hay that had been fed to the affected animals.

STREPTOTHRICOSIS, MYCOTIC DERMATITIS, AND STRAWBERRY FOOT ROT
(Species of Dermatophilus)

Streptothricosis in cattle and Mycotic Dermatitis in sheep occur in many tropical and temperate countries as acute local infections of the skin following damage by prolonged soaking, insolation, tick bites or other agencies. The condition is sometimes fatal. Diagnosis can be made by demonstrating the characteristic filaments and cocci of Dermatophilus congolensis or D. dermatonomus in the serous exudate beneath the hard scabs of the lesions. Strawberry Foot Rot in sheep has been reported only from Scotland and is thought to be caused by D. pedis. No effective treatment is known for any of the diseases but dips containing copper compounds and acaricides have been used as control measures.

Disease Names. Streptothricosis – in cattle, horse, goat. (Syn. Cutaneous actinomycosis, Impetigo, Streptomycosis; Senkobo skin disease (N. Rhodesia); ? Saria (Nyasaland); Uasin-Gishu skin disease (Kenya, Tanganyika); Kirchi (Nigeria); Drodro-Boka (Madagascar)). Dermatose contagieuse (Fr.).

Mycotic dermatitis – in sheep. (Syn. Actinomycotic dermatitis, Lumpy wool, Rain rot, Matted wool; dermatitis (Nisbet & Bannatyne, 1955)). ? Regenfäule (Ger.).

Strawberry foot rot – in sheep. (Syn. Proliferative dermatitis (Harriss, 1948)).

Pathogens. Dermatophilus congolensis Van Saceghem, 1915. Syn. Actinomyces congolensis* (Van Saceghem) Hudson, 1937 (nec (Baerts) Brumpt, 1927); Streptothrix bovis* Snijders & Jansen, 1955 (nec (Harz) Chester, 1901).

Dermatophilus dermatonomus (Bull) Austwick, 1958. Syn. Actinomyces dermatonomus Bull, 1929; Actinomyces sp. Nisbet & Bannatyne, 1955; Nocardia dermatonomus* (Bull) Henry, 1952; Polysepta dermatonomus (Bull) Thomson & Bisset, 1957.

Dermatophilus pedis (Thomson & Bisset) Austwick, 1958. Syn. Rhizobium sp. Thomson, 1954; Polysepta pedis Thomson & Bisset, 1957.

*These names were either only suggested or were used without an authority.

Hosts. Cattle (Van Saceghem, 1915); sheep (? Sinclair, 1921; Bull, 1929); goat, horse, eland (Hornby, 1920).

Geographical Distribution.

Africa, Australia, Tasmania (Oxer, 1930), New Zealand

(? Reid, 1921; Waters, 1932), India (Rajagopalan,1945), Europe (Stableforth, 1937), ? South America.

Although streptothricosis in cattle has been known in Africa for nearly fifty years and ranks there as a major disease, few mycoses have such a confused and unsatisfactory literature as this group of three caused by organisms of the same genus. The first description of the cattle disease, its pathogen and its pathology was given by Van Saceghem (1915) in the Belgian Congo and was followed (Van Saceghem, 1916) by an account of Dermatophilus congolensis, in culture. Both papers were neglected despite frequent reports of the occurrence of the condition, especially in the annual veterinary reports of many African countries. Bull (1929) described a similar organism from sheep affected by "lumpy wool" in Australia as Actinomyces dermatonomus and subsequently a closely related organism has been found in a different clinical condition in sheep by Nisbet & Bannatyne (1955). The organism causing strawberry foot rot in sheep was first described by Thomson (1954) and named Polysepta pedis by Thomson & Bisset (1957). Austwick (1958) has placed all three species in the genus Dermatophilus with D. congolensis as the type species, but calls attention to the need for a revision of the group.

The term "streptothricosis" first seems to have been applied to the disease in cattle by Henderson (1927) but it has also been used for any disease in which a narrow, filamentous and branching organism was involved, including both actinomycosis and nocardiosis as considered in this review. Previously Hutchins (1919) had attributed the disease to a "streptothrix", but as Streptothrix had already been used by Corda in 1839 for a Hyphomycete, the citation Streptothrix bovis Snijders & Jansen (1955) is invalid. The retention of the name "streptothricosis" for the disease of cattle and of "mycotic dermatitis" for that of sheep, seems justified on the grounds of their common usage (Austwick, 1958).

From many of the accounts it has not always been possible to ascertain the identity of the disease described and its relationships to any pathogen isolated. The clinical symptoms are probably diagnostic but differential diagnosis from other skin diseases has not always been carried out. The literature has been carefully studied, and it is believed that all the references cited here are of authentic cases.

Symptomatology. These three diseases are characterized by an acute or chronic inflammatory dermatitis chiefly involving the skin of the back, head, rump or the legs. The lesions vary in the different diseases and with the different animal hosts.

Cattle. The early stages of streptothricosis in cattle are revealed by the disturbance of the hair and the formation of paintbrush-like tufts (Hudson, 1937). At the base of each tuft an extensive serous exudate appears and forms a thick scab on drying. This may either be shed after a short time together with the embedded hairs or else remain attached and thicken to form an extensive crust. On removal the scabs, which are concave below, leave a moist serous patch on the skin. The distribution of the lesions is very variable, they are generally 8–10 mm. in diameter and 3–4 mm. high and extend along the length of the back, spreading gradually down the flanks and over the head and neck (Hornby, 1920; Chodnik, 1956). Sites of tick infestation are frequently affected, i. e., the axillae, groin, scrotum and udder (Plowright, 1956). Zlotnik (1955) has observed lesions following the lines of deep scratches. As the hair is not itself involved, its loss results either from removal of scabs complete with the embedded hair or else from breaking off at the surface of the hard crusts. Mornet & Thiéry (1955) recognized four clinical forms of the disease in cattle: ichthyotic, nodular (associated with Demodex infestation), tumoral and leproid.

Sheep. According to Seddon (1929) the first recognizable symptoms of mycotic dermatitis in sheep are small areas of hyperaemia which persist for 10–14 days, followed by the formation of a crust. In chronic cases, conical masses of crust material are formed on the skin, matting the wool fibres together, but usually the crust separates from the skin surface, either remaining as a zone of hardened exudate in the wool or else being cast off by the breakage of the wool fibres. On removal of the scab from an active lesion its underside is concave and a raw moist area is exposed. Bull (1929) described progressive lesions resulting in death, which may involve serious losses in lambs. Seddon (1953) reviewed the occurrence of the disease in Australia and gave new information on clinical symptoms.

The distribution of lesions on the body is very varied and often seems to be a characteristic of the particular breed of sheep, the locality, and the species and strain of the pathogen. The three related conditions in sheep are:-

(a) Mycotic dermatitis – lesions in the wool-covered parts, especially the back, sides and neck and occasionally the lips and ears. Reported from Australia (Bull, 1929; Seddon, 1929), South Africa (Bekker, 1928), India (Lall & Rajagopalan, 1949) and England (Kane et al., 1955).

(b) Dermatitis – lesions on the hairy parts of the face, or on the scrotum. Reported from Kenya (Hudson, 1937) and Scotland (Nisbet & Bannatyne, 1955).

(c) Strawberry foot rot – lesions consist of extensive inflammatory swelling of the foot from the coronet to the knee or hock, followed by thick crust formation. Reported from Scotland (Harriss, 1948; Thomson, 1954).

The few records of mycotic dermatitis in sheep from Europe may be partly explained by its benign nature in this region. Cases are not usually seen until shearing, when considerable difficulty is experienced in removing the fleece. As this operation generally takes place in dry weather the sheep rarely have active lesions, so that only the dried masses of serous exudate in the wool are seen. Such affected fleeces are down graded and lose at least a quarter of their value.

Horse. The lesions are comparable to those of cattle according to Hudson (1937) and at first 5 mm. in diameter with the hairs characteristically drawn together in groups. Later they may become confluent (Stableforth, 1937).

Goat. Beaton (1928) stated that the lesions can first be detected by palpation and occur as scabs, the size of a millet seed, which spread beneath the body and on the inner side of the legs.

Pathology. Examination of stained smears of the scabs from lesions of all three diseases reveals short lengths of narrow, divided and branching hyphae and many Gram-positive cocci, amongst numerous leucocytes and desquamated stratum corneum cells (Van Saceghem, 1915). Hudson (1937) used Giemsa stain on smears of the moist serous exudate from beneath the scabs in cattle with considerable success. Long pieces of filaments dividing first transversely and later two to three times longitudinally into coccus-like bodies, may be seen by this method. Older lesions show fewer filaments and large numbers of cocci formed by fragmentation. Sections of active lesions reveal extensive infiltration of the epidermis by mono- or polymorphonuclear leucocytes, and distension of the follicles by exudate. The scabs, in both cattle and sheep, consist of layers of pus alternating with parakeratotic stratum corneum cells (Mornet & Thiéry, 1955), whilst distributed throughout are numerous filaments and cocci.

Mycology. Isolations of Dermatophilus congolensis were first obtained by Van Saceghem (1916) by inoculation of serum broth with pulverized crusts. Hudson (1937) found that desiccation of the crusts for 9 days over concentrated sulphuric acid did not affect the viability of the organism and greatly reduced bacterial contamination. Growth in serum broth at 37°C. is rapid. During the first two days a dense mycelium of branching and tapering hyphae 1–2 micra wide develops as small fluffy spheres at the bottom of the medium. Sometimes a waxy pellicle is formed. At three days the hyphae are mostly 3–5 micra wide and have divided; first transversely into narrow segments and then two or three times longitudinally, producing up to eight cells across. Hyphae in this stage readily break up into cocci which are motile, but the exact method of their release is not yet clear. According to Thomson (1954) the motile spores of D. pedis are apically biflagellate and 0.3–0.5 micra in in diameter. On serum agar a smooth or wrinkled, shiny or matt colony is formed, which varies in colour from greyish-white to bright orange, often showing sectoring. In the first two days short aerial filaments are sometimes seen in rough colonies, but these collapse and the filaments undergo the same morphological changes as in broth cultures. Growth is good with slight beta-haemolysis on blood agar (Stableforth, 1937), but on normal mycological media, e. g. malt agar, no growth occurs. Albiston (1933) and Snijders & Jansen (1955) considered that the bovine isolates D. congolensis) could be distinguished from those from sheep (D. dermatonomus) by their more vigorous growth, their greater pathogenicity for calves, and by their colour (described by Albiston as greyish-white and by Snijders & Jansen as brown), the two types being considered as strains of one species.

Biochemical characters are not well-defined, being mostly negative. Van Saceghem (1934) found D. congolensis to be a facultative aerobe which liquefied gelatin and digested milk. Acid production (without gas) was found with glucose, sucrose, maltose and dextrin, but not with lactose, mannite, sorbite, dulcite, arabinose, laevulose, and galactose. Hudson (1937) found that acid was produced with glucose and laevulose only and, in addition to those substances listed above, raffinose, rhamnose, salacin, xylose, inulin and inositol were not fermented. D. dermatonomus has very similar biochemical characters, but D. pedis fails to liquefy gelatin, coagulate serum or ferment galactose.

Among the isolates from cases of streptothricosis of cattle which do not correspond morphologically with those of D. congolensis described above, have been Actinomyces bovis Harz var. nigerianus Erikson (1935) and the species of Streptomyces belonging to the albus series isolated by Chodnik (1956). It would appear from the description that A. bovis var. nigerianus would now also be placed in the Streptomyces series albus which includes a large group of ubiquitous saprophytic organisms. These Actinomycetes are frequently isolated from the skin of animals (Ainsworth & Austwick, 1955a), but they are not considered to be directly pathogenic. Moreover they do not appear to be even related to Dermatophilus. The identity of the organism found in association with dermatitis in turkeys by Soliman & Rollinson (1951) is also in doubt, for its cultural characters were not described and its appearance in skin section did not resemble that of D. congolensis.

Inoculation of cultures of scabs on to the skin of cattle, sheep and rabbits is generally successful but previous scarification or other damage is necessary. Bull (1929) soaked the coat of a Merino lamb for two days before inoculation, whilst Hudson (1937) plucked the hair from small areas of the skin of rabbits before rubbing in the inoculum. By this latter method a general erythema appears on the inoculated area after 72 hours and a scab forms after five days. This is shed on the ninth day and the skin heals rapidly. Hudson was unable to produce the lesions by inoculating the wool covered parts of sheep with a strain isolated from facial lesions. Stableforth (1937) stated that the isolate he obtained from a horse differed from Hudson's strain in producing discrete pustular lesions on rabbits. Typical filaments and cocci may be seen in scabs from experimental inoculations and the organism is readily re-isolated.

Serology. There is conflicting evidence on the development of immunity to these diseases. Hudson reported the resistance of rabbits to re-inoculation, and cross protection between strains of bovine and ovine origin. Curasson (1937) and Nisbet & Bannatyne (1935) found no evidence of immunity.

Epidemiology. The epidemiology of these diseases is not fully understood. The organisms have been recovered only from skin lesions on animals and although much viable material must fall from infected animals, nothing is known of their saprophytic survival in the soil or in water. There is no reliable information on transmission from animal to animal although the cattle disease, when first described, was considered to be contagious. Van Saceghem (1934) eventually concluded that this was not so, and Bull (1929) failed to establish contact infection in sheep even after 10 months' exposure of healthy animals to infected ones.

Two apparently significant epidemiological factors of possible importance are the longevity of the organisms in dried crusts (Seddon, 1929) and the production of motile spores. The former property would enable infection to persist through periods of dry weather in old scabs while on the ground and on chronically infected animals, whilst the motility of the spores would help to establish infection quickly on the return of wet conditions. Investigations into the ecology of the three species of Dermatophilus would no doubt provide a more satisfactory basis for the control of these diseases than exists at present (Simmons, 1955).

Even though adequate inoculum may be present, some damage to the skin is still apparently required for infection to occur. Constant wetting by rain is probably the main cause of damage, for infection is almost always associated with wet weather. Exposure to sunlight may also contribute.

Cattle. Among others, Schultz (1955) has been unable to correlate the disease with seasonal variation or with age, breed, sex or coat colour but zebu cattle and cattle of European origin have been regarded as more susceptible by some authors (Chodnik, 1956). The existence of a vector was suggested as long ago as 1918 (Wooldridge in Armfield, 1918) and ticks, more especially Amblyomma variegatum, were first suspected by Sinclair (1921). Subsequently Best (1928) reported that lice (Haematopinus sp.) charged with inoculum failed to infect cattle on which they fed. Plowright (1956) demonstrated a more convincing relationship between tick damage on predilection sites and the appearance of the disease in the same areas of the body. In Nyasaland, Zlotnik (1955) found few ticks and considered that the main predisposing factors were scratches from thorn bushes, for the disease did not appear in thorn-free pastures. Buck (1948) considered both ticks and thorn bush damage to be operative in Madagascar and it is possible too that tick birds (pique-boeufs, Buphagus africanus) also cause damage with their beaks.

Sheep. In sheep, shearing may also cause slight skin damage and the extensive outbreaks of mycotic dermatitis in England during June–July 1955 may have been related to this factor combined with heavy rain at shearing time.

Treatment. Effective treatment is unknown, although a great many methods have been described. When recovery occurs it is almost always spontaneous and is invariably the result of drier conditions.

Cattle. Van Saceghem (1915) first recommended the rubbing in of 3% sodium arsenite and later (1916) the use of 5–10% phenol vaseline, avoiding both friction and washing during treatment. The more recent approach has been to dip animals against tick and mite infestation, but Zlotnik (1955) found that dips containing D. D. T. and benzene hexachloride were not as effective as those containing arsenic in preventing the disease. Quaternary ammonium compounds were also used in direct applications to the lesions with some success. Plowright (1955) carried out experimental trials in the control of cattle ticks and found that this gave considerable protection from the disease, but stressed the importance of climatic factors in relation to the life-cycles of ticks and pathogen. In horses, Walker (1930) advised the repeated use of 3% copper sulphate on the lesions.

Sheep. Dips containing copper sulphate are mostly advised. Bull (1929) used 1:500 bluestone ($CuSO_4$) for an autumn dip for young animals, and compounds for topical application include 1:5000 mercuric chloride and 5% formalin ointment (Veron, 1933). The drawbacks of copper sulphate dips are described by Story (1952), who states that more than 60 p.p.m. of copper in the wool may adversely affect its dyeing qualities, and that levels of this nature are frequently attained even with 1:2000 dilutions. No treatment for strawberry foot rot has been suggested.

Economic importance. Little information is available on tne economic importance of most animal skin diseases for they are rarely fatal and are chiefly studied because of their transmission to man. Streptothricosis and mycotic dermatitis are, however, important because of their damaging effect on the hides, skins and wool from infected animals. In Kenya, Green (1956) has given figures for 8,000 goat skins, in which he rates streptothricosis second to demodectic mange as a cause of loss (9% and 14% respectively of all skins). Tanned skins and hides show thin places at lesion sites and often have deep pits in the grain surface (Dempsey, 1954). Affected leather is unsuitable for many purposes and the loss of value may be serious in countries where hides and skins are major products.

Wool values are similarly affected, but no figures can be given for the total loss in the main wool-growing areas of the world. In England a fall of 20% in the value of mildly affected wool has been reported in the finer grades (Austwick, unpublished data).

Chapter 15

RINGWORM
(Species of *Microsporum* and *Trichophyton*)

Superficial infections of keratinized layers of the skin and its appendages (hair, feathers, horns) of farm, domestic, and wild animals and birds (and also man) by a group of closely related mycelial fungi known as the dermatophytes. Though rarely if ever fatal, ringworm is at times of economic importance and while dermatophyte infections are often self-limiting they are usually intractable to treatment. Animals are a major source of ringworm infection in man.

More has been written about ringworm than about any other mycotic disease of animals and man and for no other mycosis is the older literature more confused. This confusion has been largely due to uncertainties regarding the identity of the pathogens involved and to a lack of agreement on their nomenclature. During the last decade, throughout the world, there has been a marked trend towards a more uniform treatment of these fungi but some knowledge of the historical background is still needed if use is to be made of information on ringworm and the ringworm fungi contained in older works of reference and even in the current editions of some standard text-books.

Ringworm in both animals and man is caused by dermatophytes, a group of closely related mycelial fungi imperfecti which are able to invade superficial keratinized tissues. Some dermatophytes appear to be confined to man, others are characteristic of animals. There are, however, records of man contracting infection by all the common 'animal' species and almost without exception experimental animals are susceptible to infection by 'human' species. One result of this interrelationship is the interest to medical dermatologists and to public health authorities of ringworm in animals which constitutes an important reservoir for human ringworm, especially in rural areas (see La Touche, 1955; Mortimer, 1955; Blank, 1955; Georg, 1956).

Because of the ease with which dermatophytes can be cultured, a saprophytic phase has for long been postulated. There were, however, very few records of their natural occurrence as saprophytes until the last few years when a number of dermatophytes have been isolated from the soil in different parts of the world. Some of the epidemiological implications of these observations are discussed in the sections which follow.

Most of the important dermatophytes which infect animals were first described at the turn of the century, often in rather inaccessible publications, and for a number of species the most detailed accounts are still those given by the noted French dermatologist Sabouraud (1910) in *Les Teignes* (now a rare book). Although most text-books on diseases of animals include sections on ringworm, many of these accounts are of a low standard and a comprehensive modern treatment of ringworm in animals is badly needed. The complementary pair of papers on clinical and cultural studies of animal dermatomycoses by Hoerlein (1945) and the useful practical paper by Georg (1954) on the diagnosis of ringworm in animals may be recommended as an introduction. Blank (1955) cites much of the significant recent literature and Menges & Georg (1957a) survey animal ringworm in the U.S.A. The Merck Veterinary Manual may also be consulted.

The Ringworm Fungi

The first step in the rational approach to any dermatomycosis is the identification of the fungus involved and as most dermatophytes attack more than one host it is convenient to consider briefly the mycology of the ringworm fungi before treating the clinical and epidemiological aspects of the main types of ringworm according to the animals affected.

A tentative clinical diagnosis of ringworm is confirmed by the microscopic examination -- in the clinic or in the laboratory -- of skin scrapings and hairs. This is best accomplished by making temporary mounts in 20% aqueous potash (KOH), the preparation being gently warmed if necessary before examination first under low and subsequently under higher powers of the microscope. In skin scales the septate hyphae of one dermatophyte look very much like those of another and though it is sometimes possible to make a generic diagnosis from the appearance of infected hairs, cultures have always to be made to confirm specific identification.

Cultures may be set up immediately or the samples of skin scrapings and hair may be placed in clean pieces of notepaper or envelopes for transmission to the laboratory, the dermatophytes in the tissue usually remaining viable for several weeks when dried and often for much longer periods.

Although in the parasitic phase dermatophytes are confined to keratinized tissues, ringworm fungi are not unduly specialized nutritionally and provided a supply of organic nitrogen is available (and for some species a vitamin supplement) most dermatophytes can be grown without difficulty on malt extract agar or on media similar to the peptone-glucose or peptone-maltose media which were developed by Sabouraud especially for dermatophytes.

With material from animals it is advisable to suppress bacterial growth by supplementing the media with antibacterial antibiotics (e.g. 20 units penicillin plus 40 units streptomycin per ml.) and because of the presence of vast numbers of spores of saprophytic fungi derived from hay and straw on the skins of many animals, it is necessary to use techniques which help to suppress the growth of these moulds. This may be done by pretreating the hairs with fungicides (Gentles & Dawson, 1957) or by the removal of the contaminated outer layers of the epidermal sheaths of infected hairs (Austwick, 1954), but the incorporation of cycloheximide ("Acti-dione") in the isolation medium at 0.5 mg. per ml. is probably the most effective method of control (Georg, 1954). While most dermatophytes grow most rapidly at 30° to 35°C., incubation at 25° or at laboratory temperature tends to favour fungi rather than any bacteria present.

During the first third of the twentieth century the classification of the ringworm fungi was dominated by the views of Sabouraud as summarized in *Les Teignes*, 1910. Sabouraud's taxonomic approach to the dermatophytes had a clinical bias and he recognized four genera – *Microsporum*, *Trichophyton*, *Achorion*, and *Epidermophyton* – from clinical-mycological considerations. Emmons (1934) showed that the first two and the last of Sabouraud's genera could be defined in mycological terms and that the genus *Achorion* (which comprised those dermatophytes able to cause clinical favus) was unnecessary because its constituent species could be accommodated in either *Microsporum* or *Trichophyton*. Emmons' proposals have been generally accepted both in North America and elsewhere and a further simplification has been effected by the consolidation of species and the consequent relegation of many names to synonymy. (Ainsworth (1952) pp. 19–26 may be consulted for a more detailed general discussion of the taxonomy and nomenclature of the dermatophytes.)

The single species of the genus *Epidermophyton* is confined to man and it is in the genera *Microsporum* and *Trichophyton* that the fungi causing ringworm in animals are to be found. In skin scales the branched septate hyphae of a dermatophyte are rarely diagnostic but examination of infected hairs frequently allows a generic diagnosis to be made. In *Microsporum* the hyphae break up to form an irregular mosaic of spores (arthrospores) while in *Trichophyton* the arthrospores tend to occur not in mosaics but in chains. The arthrospores of *Microsporum* form a sheath over the surface of the hair and some species of *Trichophyton* (the 'ectothrix' forms) behave in a similar way while in others (the 'endothrix' forms) the chains of arthrospores are produced within the hair – a distinction which though not absolute is a useful taxonomic guide. Another property of *Microsporum*-infected hairs which is of great help to the clinician is the characteristic greenish fluorescence of such hairs when exposed to filtered ultra-violet light (Wood's light). *Trichophyton*-infected hairs are usually non-fluorescent or fluoresce very weakly (e.g. favus hairs infected by *T. schoenleini*).

For confirmation of a generic diagnosis and for determination of the species cultures must be examined. On media such as Sabouraud's agar dermatophytes produce a number of characteristic structures and several types of spores of which the most important, because they are diagnostic for the genera, are the macroconidia. In *Microsporum* the multi-septate macroconidia are rough, thick-walled, and spindle-shaped while in *Trichophyton* they are smooth, thin-walled, and usually more or less cigar-shaped. The species are distinguished by the macroscopic and microscopic appearance of the colonies and by the size and shape of the various spores.

Although dermatophytes grow readily as saprophytes they are, in general, unstable in culture and sooner or later the characteristic spore-producing growth is replaced by a white, sterile, cottonwool-like mycelium. This phenomenon, which is known as pleomorphism and which is usually irreversible, may or may not be accompanied by a loss of pathogenicity. Pleomorphic change is encouraged by media containing sugar and is prevented or delayed by culturing on a peptone agar (Sabouraud's conservation medium) or on natural substrates such as rice or barley grains.

The species of dermatophytes, their hosts and geographical distribution are set out in Table 1 while a key for the cultural identification of the commoner ones which infect domestic and farm animals is given in Table 2.

Table 1

Dermatophytes infecting animals
(Man is susceptible to all the species listed.)

Species	Host	Distribution
Microsporum		
M. canis Bodin Syn. M. felineum Mewborn M. lanosum Sabouraud	Cat and Dog (Sabouraud, 1910, p. 204, 299; De Castro, 1928; Davidson & Gregory, 1933; La Touche, 1952a; Flores et al., 1954; Menges & Georg, 1955)	World wide
	Sheep (Jakl, 1949)	Czechoslovakia
	Monkey (Conant, 1937; as M. simiae Conant; Kral, 1955)	U.S.A.
	Chinchilla (Kral, 1955)	U.S.A.
M. audouini Gruby	Dog (Kaplan & Georg, 1957)	Europe; U.S.A.
	Monkey (Scully & Kligman, 1951)	U.S.A.
M. gypseum (Bodin) Guiart & Grigorakis Syn. Achorion gypseum Bodin M. fulvum Sabouraud	Cat (Kaplan, Georg & Bromley, 1957)	Europe; U.S.A.
	Dog (Ajello, 1953; Menges & Georg, 1957b)	France; U.S.A.
	Horse (Ajello, 1953; Thorold, 1953; Kaplan, Georg & Fosnaugh, 1956; Kaplan, Hopping & Georg, 1957)	France; Belgium; Germany; U.S.A. Madagascar; Kenya
	Fowl (Ajello, 1953)	Italy
	Guinea-pig (Shahan, 1937)	U.S.A.
	Rat (Smith, Menges & Georg, 1957)	U.S.A.
	Wild Rodents (Menges, Love, Smith & Georg, 1957)	U.S.A.
	Monkey (Ajello, 1953)	S. Pacific; Germany
	Tiger (Ajello, 1953)	Indonesia

Species	Host	Distribution
M. distortum di Menna & Marples	Dog and pet Monkeys (Kaplan, Georg, Hendricks & Leeper, 1957)	U. S. A.
M. equinum (Delacroix & Bodin) Guéguen	Horse (Sabouraud, 1910, p. 234; Krantz, 1940; Baudet, 1941; Batte & Miller, 1953)	Europe; U.S.A.
Trichophyton		
T. mentagrophytes (Robin) Blanchard Syn. T. gypseum Bodin T. asteroides Sabouraud	Cat and Dog (Georg, Roberts, Menges & Kaplan, 1957)	Europe; U.S.A.
	Cattle (Davidson, Gregory & Birt, 1934; Muende & Webb, 1937; Gentles & O'Sullivan, 1957a)	Great Britain; Canada; U.S.A.
	Horse (Sabouraud, 1910, p.357)	Europe
	Sheep (Guilhon, Charton & Durieux, 1955)	France
	Pig (McPherson, 1956)	Scotland
	Chinchilla (Blank, Byrne, Plummer & Avery, 1953 (as T. granulosum); Hayes, 1956)	U. S. A.; Canada.
	Rabbit (Vilanova & Casanovas, 1951)	Spain
	Silver Fox (Flatla, 1939; Danbolt & Mossige, 1939)	Norway
	Guinea-pig(Negroni, 1932; Mackinnon, 1949b; Menges & Georg, 1956)	Argentina; Uruguay; U.S.A.
	White Mouse (Parish & Craddock, 1931; Catanei, 1942; Booth, 1952)	Widespread in laboratories
	Rat (Smith, Menges & Georg, 1957)	U. S. A.
	Wild Rodents (Menges, Love, Smith & Georg, 1957)	U. S. A.
	Muskrat (Charles, 1940; Errington, 1942; Dozier, 1943)	U. S. A.
	Squirrel (DeLamater, 1939)	U. S. A.
	Snowshoe Hare (Adams, Salvin & Hadlow, 1956)	U. S. A.
T. equinum Gedoelst	Horse (Sabouraud, 1910, p. 388; Mackinnon, 1936; Seehawer, 1934; Baudet, 1941; Bergner, 1942; Batte & Miller, 1953; Blank, 1955; Georg, Kaplan & Camp, 1957a, b)	Europe; U. S. A. Uruguay

Species	Host	Distribution
T. gallinae (Mégnin) Silva & Benham Syn. Achorion gallinae (Mégnin) Sabouraud	Fowl (Sabouraud, 1910, p. 553; Torres & Georg, 1956; Carnaghan, Gitter & Blaxland, 1956)	France; Germany; Great Britain; U.S.A.; ? Australia (King, 1946)
	Dog (Baudet, 1940; Anon. (1943). J. Amer. vet. med. Ass., 102, 383-384)	France; French Cameroons (Catanei, 1946)
T. quinckeanum (Zopf) MacLeod & Muende Syn. Achorion quinckeanum Zopf M. quinckeanum (Zopf) Guiart & Grigorakis	Mouse (Sabouraud, 1910, p. 545; Schneider, 1954; Blank, 1957a)	) Europe;) N. America;) N. Africa;) Australia
	Cat (Blank, 1957a)	
	Sheep (Jakl, 1949)	Czechoslovakia
	Dog (Schneider, 1954; Blank, 1957a)	
	Horse (Blank, 1957a)	Germany
T. verrucosum Bodin (of which var. discoides (Sab.) Georg (syn. T. discoides Sab.) var. album (Sab.) Georg (syn. T. album Sab.) var. ochraceum (Sab.) Georg (syn. T. ochraceum Sab.) were distinguished by Ainsworth & Georg, 1954) Syn. 'T. faviforme Auct.'	Cattle (Sabouraud, 1910, p. 403; Lebasque, 1933; Blank, 1955)	World wide
	Dog (Kral, 1955; Gentles & O'Sullivan, (1957a)	Great Britain; U.S.A.
	Horse (de Magalhães, 1935; Jillson & Buckley, 1951; Ainsworth & Austwick, 1955b)	Brazil; U.S.A.; England
	Donkey (Blank, 1955)	France
	Sheep (Kral, 1955; Guilhon & Obligi, 1956)	U.S.A.; France
	Goat (Blank, 1955)	N. Africa
	Dromedary (Blank, 1955)	N. Africa

Table 2

Key to the cultural characteristics of recent isolates of the commoner dermatophytes infecting animals (Colonies grown on Sabouraud glucose agar at 25°C.)

A Macroconidia and microconidia absent .... C.
Macroconidia and/or microconidia present .... B.

B Macroconidia cigar or club-shaped, thin-walled, usually rounded at the tip; 2–10 septate; microconidia round or oval and truncated, often abundant .... Trichophyton.. D.
Macroconidia spindle-shaped, often thick-walled and encrusted, pointed at the tip, 3–14 septate; microconidia rare to abundant .... Microsporum.. G.

C Colony white, downy or cottony, pale salmon pink in reverse, usually few chlamydospores .... Microsporum audouini
Colony white or ochraceous, rarely downy, growth often submerged, very slow growing at 25°C. (faster at 37°C.), chlamydospores abundant, in chains; microconidia on thiamine-supplemented medium .... Trichophyton verrucosum

D Colony white, fast growing, surrounded by broad flat yellow margin, centre white, smooth, later pinkish or cream-coloured; reverse becoming dark reddish brown .... T. equinum
Colony white or cream-coloured, fast growing, not surrounded by a yellow margin .... E.

E Colony white, downy becoming folded with cracks along folds; macroconidia club-shaped, 1–5 septate; microconidia rare; reverse becoming rose-coloured .... T. gallinae
Colony rarely developing cracks, microconidia abundant.......... F.

F Colony white, granular or powdery, sometimes becoming buff-coloured; reverse colourless, red or yellow .... T. mentagrophytes
Colony white to cream-coloured, smooth; microconidia abundant .... T. quinckeanum

G Colony fast-growing .... H.
Colony slow-growing, aerial hyphae abundant, grey to light brown; reverse reddish brown or orange; macroconidia (on vitamin-enriched media) elongated or distorted, rare .... M. audouini

H Macroconidia 50–75 μ x 12–25 μ with up to 14 septa; colony at first white, fluffy, with aerial mycelium profuse, normally bright yellow or orange in reverse .... M. canis
Macroconidia 40–55 μ x 12-15 μ with up to 8 septa, colony granular, buff-coloured; macroconidia abundant, reddish-brown in reverse .... M. gypseum
Macroconidia 25–35 μ x 18–20 μ, colony pale yellow at first with little aerial mycelium, turning brownish with age .... M. equinum

Cat and Dog Ringworm

Symptomatology. The clinical manifestation of ringworm in cats is often inconspicuous (Fuentes, Bosch & Boudet, 1954). This is particularly so for Microsporum canis infections when attention may first be drawn to an infected animal by the development of ringworm in a human contact. At other times there is a mild, non-inflammatory scaling, bare patches showing broken hairs, or a more inflammatory reaction leading to obvious crust formation (see La Touche, 1953). Rarely there are kerion-like lesions but in cases of Trichophyton quinckeanum infection favic scutula may develop. Lesions are frequent on the face and paws, the whiskers may become infected, and La Touche (1955) has recorded the infection of the claws of a cat by M. canis (a similar infection in the dog was noted by Young, 1956). In severe cases there may be a more generalized infection with lesions on several parts of the body. In dogs, the symptoms tend to be more obvious than in cats; circular lesions up to 2.5 cm. in diameter appearing on any part of the body.

Diagnostic clinical differences between infections by Microsporum canis and T. mentagrophytes have not yet been defined but scutula in both cats and dogs suggest T. quinckeanum infection.

Diagnosis. M. canis infected hairs show a characteristic greenish fluorescence under ultra-violet light filtered through cobalt glass (Wood's light) and this greatly facilitates diagnosis, particularly where the whole animal may be examined. Fluorescent hairs may be easily removed and examined microscopically and placed in culture. Infection due to Trichophyton mentagrophytes cannot be detected under Wood's light and so scrapings of the lesions should be examined for the occurrence of hairs with basal sheaths of epidermal cells. The presence of the characteristic arthrospore sheaths or merely of hyphae in or on the hairs or skin scales is sufficient for a provisional diagnosis but cultural confirmation is always needed. M. audouini infections are detected in the same way. M. gypseum infected cat hairs do not fluoresce according to Kaplan, Georg & Bromley (1957), and for such infections as for Trichophyton infections the confirmation of ringworm is by the microscopic examination of hairs and skin scales.

Mycology. M. canis, probably the most frequent dermatophyte infecting cats and dogs, is very easily obtained in pure culture on any standard mycological medium and can be identified by the production of yellow pigment and the profuse production of spindle-shaped macroconidia. M. gypseum, M. distortum and M. audouini (the last two recorded from dogs only) are also easily cultured and T. mentagrophytes and T. quinckeanum likewise present no difficulties (see Table 2).

In addition to the above species T. gallinae has been recorded occasionally from dogs (see Table 1). Other records for dogs which are of unknown significance include Oospora canina Sabrazès (see Sabouraud, 1910, p. 569; Branchini, 1935) causing favus; T. caninum Matruchot & Dassonville (Sabouraud, 1910, p. 395); Aleurisma vuillemini Grigoraki, Fayet & Magrou (1926) from a sore on the head; Eidamella actoni Datta [nom. nud.] (1932); and T. rubrum (Castellani) Ota reported by Chakraborty et al. (1954); while Microsporon sapporense has been described from the cat in Japan by Komuro et al. (1952). T. schoenleini (Lebert) Langeron & Milochevitch, the cause of favus in man, has also been recorded from both cats (see Blank, 1955) and dogs (Catanei, 1936).

Epidemiology. Cats and dogs are the usual hosts of M. canis and it is possible that the reservoir of infection is endemic infection among these animals. Man frequently contracts infection from cats and dogs but man to man transfer appears to be limited. T. mentagrophytes is likewise commonly found on cats and dogs but this species has a very wide and diverse host range (see Table 1) so that cats and dogs may possibly contract infection from other animal hosts and from the soil. M. audouini and T. schoenleini and T. rubrum – dermatophytes characteristic of man – are very rarely recorded from cats and dogs (or other animals), and when they are, infection from man seems to be the most likely explanation. Outbreaks of ringworm due to M. gypseum on the other hand are of world-wide distribution but are sporadic in both man and animals and as this dermatophyte appears to be widely distributed in soil (see Ajello, 1953) it seems probable that the soil is the reservoir of infection.

The incubation period for M. canis infection in cats and dogs is 14–28 days but, as already noted, the signs of infection may be very inconspicuous and are probably to some extent at least conditioned by the physiological state of the host. de Almeida et al. (1950) claimed that under experimental conditions lesions of M. canis infection in cats were intensified by a vitamin-deficient diet and decreased again on return to a full diet. They also drew attention to the fact that while on the deficient diet the cats lost their sexual activity and this suggests a possible parallel with human infections by M. audouini which are characteristic of children and resolve spontaneously at puberty. It also seems likely that cats and dogs, like man, are at least for a time immune or resistant after recovery from an attack of ringworm.

Treatment. Ringworm in animals (as in man), particularly in experimental infections, is often eliminated spontaneously. At other times infection seems to persist in cats at a subclinical level for months or even years or it may become generalized in animals in a very poor condition. This is perhaps the reason for, rather than the result of, the severe symptoms and most infected cats and dogs are probably destroyed. The first essential of any treatment is to isolate the animal. Success has been claimed for painting the lesions with tincture of iodine or the use of a sulphur dust. Kirk (1946) recorded a cure with a phenyl mercuric chloride ointment. With dogs regular washing with a detergent (a method useful with cattle, horses and guinea-pigs – see below) would probably merit trial. There is no evidence, as there is for human infections, that one species of dermatophyte is more intractable than another but no data are available on the treatment of ringworm in cats and dogs under controlled conditions.

Symptomatology. The lesions are discrete and vary in size from circular patches 1 cm. or less in diameter to extensive areas. Sometimes there is only scaliness and loss of hair. More usually the lesions, at first white, develop thick, yellowish-brown, asbestos-like crusts. Lesions occur most frequently on the head and, particularly, the neck (Ford, 1956; Gentles & O'Sullivan, 1957b) but the flanks, rump and limbs may be involved.

Pathology. The histopathology has been little studied. The most recent account is that by Sellers, Sinclair & La Touche (1956), who reported that in the early stages of invasion of the skin of calves by Trichophyton verrucosum there was extensive proliferation of the mycelium in the stratum corneum including that of the hair follicles. The sheath of spores enclosing each hair was found to arise by transverse fragmentation of a mycelial network which sometimes seemed to originate in the mycelial weft at the mouth of the follicle or in the intrafollicular stratum corneum. The cortex of the hair was penetrated and hyphae grew as far as the zone in which keratinization was taking place (cf. La Touche, 1952b).

There was a marked inflammatory response to invasion by the fungus. This was accompanied by extensive proliferation of the stratum corneum into which inflammatory exudate had infiltrated. Many papillae were surmounted by stratified accumulations of parakeratotic cells dilated with serum. Later, intradermal and intra-epidermal micro-abscesses were formed around infected follicles. Many intra-epidermal abcesses ruptured beneath the stratum corneum to give extensive pools of exudate containing large numbers of leucocytes.

Mycology. The usual cause of cattle ringworm throughout the temperate regions of the world is Trichophyton verrucosum. A clinical diagnosis of ringworm can be confirmed by mounting hairs from lesions in caustic potash when infected hairs are seen to be sheathed by spores 2–8 micra in diameter which, in early infections, are seen to be arranged in linear series.

For specific identification cultures have to be made and the isolation of T. verrucosum in pure culture often gives much trouble, because this species is slow growing and has rather exacting nutritional requirements (see Georg, 1950) and because the skin of cattle is usually heavily contaminated with the spores of saprophytic moulds as well as bacteria. A number of special isolation methods have been devised such as the ox-bile agar of Littman (1947) and the addition to the medium of "Acti-dione" (cycloheximide) by Georg (1954). Others are noted by Austwick (1954), who described a technique for removing the spore sheath in a drop of sterile water and then inoculating nutrient agar containing penicillin and streptomycin with the resulting spore suspension. On the commonly employed media numerous chlamydospores but no macroconidia are produced. A more profuse aerial growth and macroconidial development occurs on vitamin-supplemented media (Mackinnon & Artagaveytia-Allende, 1948; Georg, 1950).

Sabouraud (1910) distinguished three animal species of the so-called 'faviform' group of Trichophyton as T. album, T. ochraceum, and T. discoides, all of which have been recorded from cattle. During recent years these forms have been frequently referred to, particularly in North America, by the illegitimate group name 'T. faviforme' (Georg, 1950) and Ainsworth & Georg (1954) proposed that Sabouraud's species should be treated as varieties of T. verrucosum Bodin.

T. mentagrophytes which commonly affects dogs and cats (see p.87), many other animals (see below), and man appears to be very rare in cattle. Davidson, Gregory & Birt (1934) have recorded this species from cattle in Canada; Muende & Webb (1937) from England. Among other dermatophytes recorded from cattle are T. villosum (from China) and T. papillosum (Syria and Morocco), both described by Lebasque (1933, 1934), Grubyella camerounensis Ota & Gaillard (1926) (Cameroons), and T. megnini (Brazil, Salles Gomes, Freitas & Cunha (1954); Germany, see Blank, 1955).

Immunology. There are few precise data on the immunology of cattle ringworm. Sellers et al. (1956) showed that experimental infection confers a resistance to re-infection, at least for a time, and this conclusion is also that of Ford (1956) from field observations.

Epidemiology. It is commonly held that calves are more susceptible to ringworm than are older animals (McPherson, 1957a) and that the incidence of the disease is higher in winter than in summer. That the disease is frequently severe in calves is supported by many observations but there seems to be little evidence that calves are intrinsically more susceptible than adult animals and Ainsworth & Austwick (1955a) found no evidence of any marked seasonal periodicity of outbreaks of cattle ringworm in Great Britain. Infection seems to be contracted by contact of healthy with diseased animals and with contaminated walls and woodwork of the buildings. (Walker (1955) made isolations of T. verrucosum from the latter.) Calves are commonly kept confined so that there are many opportunities for spread of the infection and for constant re-infection within a group of animals and for an infected group of calves to contaminate the environment. McPherson (1957b) has shown that T. verrucosum retains its viability for up to four and a half years in skin scrapings so that a building disused during the summer months would still contain much infected material in the following autumn. Further, McPherson showed for T. verrucosum that in skin scales 1.5 mm. thick the spores were protected from the action of ultra-violet light equivalent to 437 hours of midday, midsummer sunshine in medium latitudes. The spread of T. verrucosum is therefore not likely to be influenced by summer sunshine but the fewer contacts between one animal and another in the field might well account for the few records of epidemic outbreaks while the animals are at grass.

As dermatophytes are able to grow on many substrates it is possible that they might also persist as saprophytes on the farm, and Muende & Webb (1937) recorded T. mentagrophytes growing on dung in a building in which cattle infected by this species had been housed. T. verrucosum does not appear to have been recovered from this substrate or from soil.

Contraction of infection by man from infected cattle is frequent (e.g. Jillson & Buckley, 1951; Blank, 1953; Blank & Craig, 1954; Gentles & O'Sullivan, 1957b) and is an important aspect of the epidemiology of human ringworm, but transmission of infection in the reverse direction probably never occurs.

Treatment. It is probably safe to state that there is at present no satisfactory treatment for cattle ringworm. Ford (1956) found ringworm lesions to persist for 10–17 weeks in a field outbreak (a value similar to that obtained by Austwick in unpublished observations on experimental infections). He suggests that there was little evidence to show that any treatment shortened this period and unpublished observations by McPherson and by Austwick have confirmed that the topical treatment of lesions has little effect on their natural course.

Among the many treatments that have been advocated, spraying the animals (both infected and healthy) with a fungicide (Baker & Davis (1954) used 0.45–0.5 lb. of captan /20 gal. at 1.0–1.5 gal. / animal) washes away and possibly sterilizes much infected material and thus no doubt greatly reduces the reservoir of infection even if it does not greatly affect the course of established infections. A similar result has been claimed for the use of detergents. It will be apparent that much can be done to reduce the chances of infection by the thorough cleaning of calf sheds and success has been claimed in breaking a succession of epidemics among calves kept in a particular shed by spraying both walls and woodwork with Bordeaux mixture or other copper-containing fungicide (Ainsworth & Austwick, unpublished).

Ringworm of Horses

Symptomatology. The typical signs are dry raised scaling lesions on any part of the animal, but particularly the saddle and girth regions and the hindquarters, leading to circumscribed bare patches. Adjacent lesions may become confluent but areas of infection are never so extensive or so heavily crusted as in cattle ringworm. Often the lesions appear as small inflamed swellings with development of pus and the affected animals have considerable discomfort ('girth itch'). Recent publications illustrating the symptoms of equine ringworm include those of Hoerlein (1945) and Georg, Kaplan & Camp (1957a,b).

Diagnosis and Mycology. Ringworm in horses is caused by a number of different dermatophytes but at present it does not seem to be possible to distinguish the particular species implicated from the clinical picture. Species of both *Trichophyton* and *Microsporum* are involved. The presence of a sheath of spores around each infected hair shows all infections to be of the 'ectothrix' type while the arrangement of the spores in chains rather than as a mosaic distinguishes infections by the first genus from those due to the second. Infections by *M. equinum* are distinguished by the characteristic fluorescence of affected hairs in Wood's light. *Trichophyton* infections and infections by *M. gypseum* do not fluoresce.

Both species of *Microsporum* are easily isolated on any of the usual media. Both produce abundant macroconidia of which the thick-walled, spindle-shaped, 6 to 10-celled macroconidia of M. equinum are easily distinguished from the smaller, thin-walled, blunt-ended, 3 to 4-celled macroconidia of M. gypseum.

Although T. mentagrophytes was the first species of Trichophyton to be recorded from the horse (in 1893, see Sabouraud, 1910) T. equinum is more commonly recorded as causing equine ringworm. T. verrucosum has only occasionally been recorded from horses (see Table 1). The form of T. mentagrophytes is generally the one which gives a colony with a granular surface (the T. granulosum of Sabouraud = the T. mentagrophytes var. granular of Georg). This species is autotrophic for vitamins and in this respect differs from T. equinum which is unique among dermatophytes in having an absolute requirement for nicotinic acid (Georg, 1949), a requirement which is satisfied by the hair of horses, donkeys, and mules but not by the hair of man or other animals. T. equinum is also distinguished from T. mentagrophytes by the larger size of the spores which sheathe infected hair; 3.5–8.0 micra as against 3.0–5.0 micra.

Among other dermatophytes which have been recorded from the horse is T. bullosum Lebasque (1933, 1934) from Syria, Tunisia and the Sudan.

[For additional references to this section see Table 1 and the review by Georg, Kaplan & Camp (1957b).]

Epidemiology. As the transmission of ringworm among horses is probably chiefly by the contact of healthy with infected animals, equine ringworm is characteristic of large stables. This being so it is hardly surprising that ever since the time of Dassonville (who was veterinarian to the 12me Régement d'Artillerie and who with Matruchot was the first, in 1898, to describe but not to name T. equinum) there has been a series of reports by military veterinarians on epidemic outbreaks of ringworm among army horses (Brocq-Rousseu, Urbain & Barotte (1927) in France; Neefs & Gillain (1931) in Belgium; Bergner (1942) in Germany). The disease is also common among racehorses which are constantly being moved from one racecourse to another. Lomas (1939) drew attention to the severity of the disease in stables where one man attends to 10–12 horses and uses the same tools for each, a position which is aggravated if two shifts are worked when it would be possible to transfer infection to up to twenty or more horses a day. The incubation period appears to vary from 10 days (Lomas, 1939) to some 3 weeks (Ainsworth & Austwick, 1955a).

M. gypseum, as already mentioned apparently inhabits soil from which an infection could have its origin but neither M. equinum nor T. equinum appears to have been found as a saprophyte. The rare T. verrucosum infections have no doubt originated from infected cattle.

Treatment. As for cattle ringworm, it is rather doubtful if topical treatment influences the course of infection which may persist for 8 weeks or more although such treatment may greatly reduce the amount of infection. Batte & Miller (1953) claim to have successfully treated animals with ortho tack wash, a detergent, at 2 oz./24 pints of water. Faure (1939) advocated searing single lesions with a blunt ended iron heated to dull red.

Probably the disinfection of stables by washing down with a disinfectant or the use of a blowlamp on walls, etc. is an essential procedure in ensuring that infection does not recur.

Ringworm of Sheep, Goats and Pigs

Sheep. There are few records of ringworm of sheep and there is no comprehensive account of the symptomatology. In the outbreaks recorded, small crusted lesions have usually been reported on the face and head (Catanei, 1931; Guilhon, Charton & Durieux, 1955). There seems to be no record of any serious infection of the wool. White, Mandels & Siu (1950), who made a comprehensive laboratory study of the degradation of woollen fabrics by fungi and reviewed the literature, found wool to be easily attacked by *Microsporum gypseum* but this species does not seem to have been recorded from sheep.

Jakl (1949) isolated *M. canis* and *Trichophyton quinckeanum* from sheep with a skin disease which was possibly ringworm; Catanei (1931) described an isolate of *Trichophyton* from a sheep in Algeria as a new species under the name *T. pruinosum* and recorded *T. verrucosum* (as *T. discoides*) from sheep in the same region (Catanei, 1939). From the two small outbreaks in France recently recorded by Guilhon *et al.* (1955) (3 sheep in a flock of 300) and by Guilhon & Obligi (1956) (about a dozen of 120 infected) *T. mentagrophytes* (as *T. granulosum*) was isolated.

No particular treatment can be recommended. In the last outbreak mentioned above the lesions resolved in 4–5 weeks.

Goat. The only record of ringworm in a goat noted in the literature is the record of *Trichophyton langeroni* infection of a child in Algeria contracted from a goat with ringworm (Catanei & Izac, 1941).

Pig. There are various references to 'ringworm' in pigs in handbooks on pig breeding but the only recent and authentic record of ringworm in pigs is that by McPherson (1956) from Scotland. The affected animals had circular reddened areas on the neck and sides of the trunk without loss of hair. Infection of hairs by *Trichophyton mentagrophytes* was confirmed by microscopy and culture. The lesions resolved spontaneously after 10 weeks.

Ringworm of the Camel

Ringworm in the camel is briefly reviewed by Curasson (1947, p. 371). This condition is not well understood and the status of *Trichophyton langeroni* (*Grubyella langeroni* Baudet) and *Aleurisma lugdunense* Vuil. (from dromedaries from Algeria in the Hague zoological gardens) (Baudet, 1930a, b) and *T. dankaliense* Castellani (1937) (from a piece of camel skin) is uncertain.

Fowl Favus

Symptomatology. The symptoms of this well-known but very rarely seen disease are characteristically a thick white crusting of the comb and wattles but in severe cases the infection may become generalized involving the bases of the feathers and the development of circular favic lesions on the underlying skin. In recent cases (Carnaghan, Gitter & Blaxland, 1956; Torres & Georg, 1956) the symptom expression has been less severe than in the classical description by Sabouraud, Suis & Suffran (1909; and repeated by Sabouraud, 1910). In Great Britain, according to Carnaghan *et al.* (1956), a clinically similar but milder condition of unknown aetiology with which the true fowl favus has recently been confused is more prevalent.

Pathology. The pathology has been described in some detail by Sabouraud (1910). The white crusts are fungal in nature and similar to the scutula of favus in man. The infection is confined to the keratinized tissue and there is little tissue reaction.

Mycology. The causal agent was first described by Mégnin in France in 1881 as *Epidermophyton gallinae*. Sabouraud used the binomial *Achorion gallinae* (the name which appears in most text-books) and it was Silva & Benham (June 1952) who first classified this dermatophyte as *Trichophyton gallinae* in the course of a nutritional study on this fungus. (Two months later Georg (1952) published her results of a similar study and also made the combination *T. gallinae*.)

T. gallinae is autotrophic for vitamins and is easily cultured. The colonies, at first white and flat, become tinged with pink later and a red pigment diffuses into the medium; the degree of pigment production depending, according to Silva & Benham (1952), on the concentration of lysine. The macroconidia, which may be numerous, are usually club-shaped, 5 to 10-celled and up to 50 micra in length.

Epidemiology. Fowl favus has a world-wide distribution (see Table 1) but its occurrence is sporadic. It is markedly contagious but the reservoir of infection is unknown. The infection is transmissible to man (Sabouraud, 1910; Torres & Georg, 1956). Guinea-pigs are normally susceptible to experimental inoculation (Torres & Georg, 1956) but Carnaghan *et al.* (1956) were unable to infect either guinea-pigs or rabbits.

Treatment. Removal of the crusts with soap and water followed by treatment with a disinfectant (*e.g.* phenol, iodine, etc.) has been recommended. Isolation of infected birds and attention to general hygiene is probably of major importance in eradicating and preventing outbreaks.

Ringworm of Rodents and Laboratory Animals

The common laboratory animals – particularly the guinea-pig and the mouse – are susceptible to experimental inoculation with most dermatophytes whether from man or animals. Spontaneous outbreaks of ringworm among these experimental animals are not uncommon (although they are not usually considered to merit being recorded in the literature) and there are numerous reports of proved or probable ringworm infection in rodents and other small animals, both in the wild and in captivity. The following notes draw attention to some of the more important and useful of these records.

Mouse. The classical ringworm of the mouse is 'mouse favus' caused by Trichophyton quinckeanum. Natural infection results in white crusted lesions on the head and body — lesions which may be very extensive. This condition has a wide geographical distribution (see Table 1) and in most countries there are records of the infection being transmitted from mice to domestic animals and to man. T. quinckeanum has recently been studied by Vanbreuseghem (1950), and by Blank (1957a) who has comprehensively reviewed the literature.

Laboratory mice are usually infected by T. mentagrophytes (Parish & Craddock, 1931; Catanei, 1943). The symptoms are typically inconspicuous and the first indication of ringworm in a stock of mice may be the infection of laboratory attendants. T. mentagrophytes has also been recorded from wild mice (Menges, Love, Smith & Georg, 1957).

Guinea-pig. Negroni (1932) recorded a natural infection of guinea-pigs in Argentina by Trichophyton mentagrophytes (as T. lacticolor) and Mackinnon (1949b) in Uruguay and Menges & Georg (1956) in the U.S.A. have given details of outbreaks of ringworm in laboratory guinea-pigs caused by the same dermatophyte. The symptoms in guinea-pigs, as in mice, may be inconspicuous (Fuentes & Aboulafia, 1955). Menges, Georg & Habermann (1957) have advocated weekly dipping in 1:200 ortho tack wash as a control measure.

Shahan (1937) recorded Microsporum gypseum from the guinea-pig.

Chinchilla. Outbreaks of 'fur slipping' of chinchillas in Canada caused by Trichophyton mentagrophytes have been described by Blank, Byrne, Plummer & Avery (1953) and by Hayes (1956) in the U.S.A. Hayes advocates treatment with "Vioform" (iodochlorohydroxyquinoline).

Hare. Adams, Salvin & Haddow (1956) have noted Trichophyton mentagrophytes in a natural population of snowshoe hares (Lepus americana) in Montana.

Rat. Trichophyton mentagrophytes and Microsporum gypseum have been recorded by Menges, Love, Smith & Georg (1957) and Smith, Menges & Georg (1957) from various species of wild rats in Georgia.

Muskrat. Ringworm of muskrats caused by Trichophyton mentagrophytes has been recorded in the U.S.A. by Charles (1940), Errington (1942), and Dozier (1943).

S q u i r r e l. DeLamater (1939) confirmed a *Trichophyton mentagrophytes* infection of a common grey squirrel on the campus of Johns Hopkins University.

S i l v e r F o x. Outbreaks of *Trichophyton mentagrophytes* ringworm on silver fox farms in Norway are noted by Flatla (1939) and Danbold & Mossige (1939).

M o n k e y. Among the dermatophytes recorded from monkeys are *Microsporum gypseum* (as *M. fulvum*) (Hasegawa & Yamamoto, 1936), *M. canis* (as *M. simiae*) (Conant, 1937), *M. audouini* (Scully & Kligman, 1951), *M. distortum* (Kaplan, Georg, Hendricks & Leeper, 1957) and *Trichophyton mentagrophytes* (Emmons, 1940).

Chapter 16

MOULD TOXICOSES AND POISONOUS FUNGI
(excluding ergotism)

Besides ergot (Claviceps purpurea) (see p. 106), certain other fungi are known to produce substances toxic to animals. One group of toxicoses is due to the ingestion of food damaged by the growth of moulds and another is due to eating toxin-containing fruit-bodies of larger fungi. A variety of symptoms are exhibited by the affected animals but internal haemorrhage, nervous disturbance, vomiting and hyperkeratosis are the most frequently reported, and occasionally sudden death. Only fifteen toxicoses have been definitely associated with specific fungi and for few of these has any attempt been made to identify the toxin involved.

The poisoning of animals by fungi may take place in a number of ways including:

(a) poisoning by feedingstuffs affected after harvesting by the growth of known and unknown toxin-producing fungi.
(b) poisoning following grazing on herbage or crops affected by plant pathogenic fungi.
(c) poisoning by larger fungi, i. e., mushrooms and toadstools.
(d) poisoning by the indirect toxic effects (chiefly respiratory) of the ingestion and inhalation of smut and rust spores from infected fodder.

The only comprehensive review of mycotoxicoses is the one in Russian by Sarkisov (1954) and this is not available for easy reference. The work deals with many aspects of the conditions recognized in the U.S.S.R. and devotes other chapters to unspecified types of poisoning not yet proved to be due to fungi. The toxicoses are described under 10 separate headings according to their causal fungi and there are 268 references in Russian and 32 in other languages. Apart from this study few attempts have been made to gather together the scattered accounts of fungus poisoning in animals. The most notable contribution to the literature in the English language has been by Steyn (1933), who has given an excellent introduction to the subject as well as including details of feeding experiments on 86 animals carried out with mouldy feedingstuffs at Onderstepoort.

Poisoning by Feedingstuffs, Grazing, and Inhalation

(For convenience these toxicoses are considered alphabetically under specific and unidentified fungi.)

Diagnosis. Diagnosis of this type of poisoning presents many difficulties, and the authentic cases reported have almost always entailed a detailed investigation of the fungi present in the sample of food and toxicity tests with the individual species. Sufficient information however is now available for cases of internal haemorrhage, nervous symptoms and severe intestinal disturbance not attributable to any other causes, to be regarded as suspected fungal poisoning, and undoubtedly less exacting methods of diagnosis will be devised.

The methods of testing feedingstuffs for the presence of fungal toxins are given by Sarkisov (1954) but are also described by Carll et al. (1953). They consist of the oral dosage of experimental animals with known quantities of the suspected food and dermal testing using extracts obtained after refluxing in a Soxhlet apparatus. In addition it is necessary to isolate and identify the moulds present in the foodstuff and to test individually each species by feeding and skin tests using extracts from both the mycelium from pure culture and the substrate on which the fungus has been grown. Dermal testing has chiefly been carried out on rabbits in which the skin of the flank is shaved and an ether extract applied in olive oil. The degree and progress of the reaction over the next few days is then noted. Further tests have sometimes been carried out on the toxin including its toxicity for mice by various routes and examination for antibiotic activity (Forgacs et al., 1954), but only in very few cases have the toxins been chemically identified.

Microbiological Aspects. The colonization of the soil and of plant and animal substrates by fungi inevitably leads to intense microbial competition for the different complex organic nutrients available and it seems that the excretion and accumulation of substances antagonistic to other micro-organisms is of considerable advantage in obtaining maximum growth against competitors. The antagonistic substances are now termed antibiotics and their production by fungi is sufficiently well known to be considered the rule rather than the exception. Many antibiotics are known which are too toxic for therapeutic use and it seems likely that it is substances of this nature which are basically responsible for outbreaks of poisoning attributed to mouldy food.

A feature of this type of poisoning is that it is sporadic and appears to be largely dependent on the occurrence of weather favourable for the growth of the toxin-producing fungus. Outbreaks of the fusario-toxicoses, cornstalk disease and vulvovaginitis in sows, have almost always followed bad harvesting seasons whilst it is clear that the degree of mouldiness of hay varies from year to year according to prevalence of wet conditions during harvesting. The weather prevailing at the time of gathering the crop therefore seems to play a major part in its subsequent spoilage by moulds and hence to both the occurrence of the toxicoses described here and of several of the respiratory mycoses described in other sections.

Identified Species of Fungi.

Aspergillus – Perhaps because of their importance as pathogens, the toxin production by species of this genus has been studied more closely than most others. The earlier records of toxicity centred around the investigations of Ceni & Besta (1902), whose interest was in the pathogenic mechanism of *A. fumigatus* infection. They obtained toxic substances by alcohol and ether extraction of the spores of this fungus, but their significance was not pursued further. *A. fumigatus* is probably the most abundant of all toxin-producing species found in mouldy food and Carll et al. (1955) experimentally produced extensive internal haemorrhage in a calf after feeding with artificially infected maize for 20 days. Extracts of the maize also showed toxicity for the skin of rabbits. Outbreaks of hyperkeratosis in calves were attributed by Forgacs et al. (1954) to the growth of toxin-producing strains of A. clavatus in pelleted foodstuffs. They isolated this fungus and caused the death of two calves by feeding them on whole grain inoculated with the isolate. Characteristic lesions of internal haemorrhage were produced whilst sub-lethal doses led to hyperkeratosis. Similar results were obtained by Carll et al. (1954) for certain isolates of A. chevalieri. Levitski & Koniukhova (1947) added A. flavus, A. nidulans and A. niger to the list of toxin-producing species. Carll et al. (1954) failed to obtain results with strains of A. flavus and A. tamarii also isolated from mouldy food concentrate but Burnside et al. (1957) found that their strains of A. flavus produced substrates which were toxic for pigs.

Dendrodochium toxicum — Toxicosis due to Dendrodochium toxicum has been described only in the U.S.S.R., where it was first observed in 1937 among horses in the Ukraine. The fungus infects straw and chaff and the disease runs a very rapid, fatal course (Sarkisov, 1954; Karpova-Benua, 1954).

Diplodia zeae -- Mitchell (1918a) found that maize infected by Diplodia zeae could cause incoordination and paralysis when fed to cattle. Symptoms appeared within two days of feeding 20 lb. of experimentally inoculated maize to one animal. Theiler (1927) considered that cattle and sheep were affected, and gave catarrhal enteritis and hyperaemia of the lungs and kidneys as characteristics of this toxicosis. Mitchell & Beadles (1940) have repeated the earlier work on the impaired feeding value of maize damaged by this fungus.

Fusarium — The fusariotoxicoses are fairly well known and four species of Fusarium and their varieties have been found to produce toxins. Toxin-producing strains of F. sporotrichioides have been recognized only in the U.S.S.R., where they were found growing on grain which had over-wintered in the field under snow. Such affected grain fed to animals produced "alimentary toxic anaemia" characterized by haemorrhages in the alimentary canal. Horses, pigs and dogs have been affected, but the most serious outbreaks have occurred in man (Sarkisov (1954) lists 92 references on this toxicosis). Loginov (1958) isolated F. sporotrichioides var. minus from mouldy wheat bran fed to newly-weaned piglets which had died with acute catarrhal inflammation of the naso-pharynx, stomatitis, oedema of the lungs and liver dystrophy.

Steyn (1933) made an extensive series of experiments using F. moniliforme -- var. subglutinans -- by feeding the fungus and its substrates to rabbits. Only two died, but these showed paralytic symptoms for the previous two days.

F. graminearum (syn. F. roseum), the imperfect state of Gibberella saubinetii (syn. G. zeae ?), causes scab of barley and other cereals, forming the perithecia of its perfect state on the grains. Affected barley has proved toxic when fed to most species of domestic animals and also to man but the toxicosis is best known in pigs. Although its toxic properties were known previously, it was the extensive infection of the North American barley crop in 1928 that led to outbreaks of poisoning in pigs both in that region and in Europe, to which quantities of the same grain were exported. Some 20 papers on the disease in pigs appeared during the subsequent three years, and nearly all described symptoms of vomiting, refusal to eat and foetid diarrhoea which occurred within a short time of feeding. Schroeter & Strassberger (1931) considered cholin or a hydrolysed ester to be the toxin but the precise nature of the substance was not established. It was apparently not formed in pure cultures on artificially infected grain and Moore et al. (1934) stated that "the toxic principle results from the interaction of parasite and host during the active growing period". In man there is a distinct effect on the central nervous system giving rise to staggering and hence to the name "drunken bread" for loaves prepared from infected barley (Sarkisov, 1954).

Stachybotrys alternans (syn. S. atra ?) – Although species of Stachybotrys are common saprophytes on plant substrates and are world-wide in distribution, one strain has been found to produce stachybotryotoxicosis. This is S. alternans Bon. var. jateli and it has so far been found only in Eastern Europe and the U.S.S.R. The earliest records of the disease came from Russia in 1938 and the disease was studied extensively by Vertinskii (1940) but most of the information here is taken from Sarkisov's account. S. alternans var. jateli when growing on straw or hay produces a toxin in 2–3 weeks, just about the same time as spore formation occurs. When affected fodder is fed to horses symptoms of the disease appear in 1–4 days and consist of cracking and swelling of the lips and inflammation of the oral mucosa (1st stage). Continued feeding leads to extensive changes in the blood including a fall in the leucocyte count and a loss of clotting power, whilst later necrotic foci appear in the mouth (2nd stage). The 3rd and final phase of the disease follows with a sudden rise in temperature to 40° – 41°C., increased heart action, further deterioration of the blood, and death in 1–3 days. Post-mortem examination reveals extensive haemorrhages in many organs including the brain, and necrosis of the alimentary tract. The disease has received considerable attention in the U.S.S.R. and measures for its control have been devised, largely based on the recognition of affected fodder and its destruction.

Penicillium – The penicillia are by far the best known antibiotic-producing fungi, but several of the antibiotics are highly toxic for animals as well as being active against bacteria. Among these is patulin isolated originally from P. patulum, but considered by Hori et al. (1954) to be the cause of mass deaths in cows which had eaten malt feed affected by a Penicillium sp. of the urticae series. Sippel et al. (1954) described a haemorrhagic disease of pigs and cattle which followed the feeding of mouldy corn (maize) and they were later able to reproduce the condition by feeding maize on which the fungi isolated from the original sample had been grown (Burnside et al., 1957). These authors found that only two of the 13 species of moulds which they isolated from the mouldy maize produced any toxins, viz. Aspergillus flavus and Penicillium rubrum. Four pigs force-fed 8 ounces of maize infected by the latter species, died within 24 hours and similar rapid results were obtained in a goat, mice and horses. Non-toxic strains of the same species were also isolated.

Puccinia graminis – The rust fungi (Uredinales) have occasionally been responsible for reports of poisoning in livestock (Friedberger & Fröhner, 1905), and recently Lapčevič et al. (1953) have given an account of how five of 16 horses died suddenly following the feeding of severely-rusted wheat straw infected with Puccinia graminis; the remaining 11 animals had salivation and stomatitis. Attempts at the experimental reproduction of the condition resulted in the death of one of three horses.

Ustilago and Tilletia – The spores of the smut fungi (Ustilaginales) occur in large quantities in affected grain and have occasionally been found to cause disease which might possibly be termed a toxicosis but is probably more correctly classed as an allergy which may possibly develop into a true mycosis. Steyn (1933), quoting Pammel (1911), refers to the feeding of maize infected with Ustilago maydis (syn. U. zeae) as a cause of loss of condition in cattle. Hutyra & Marek (1922) say that the same fungus was responsible for gout in birds, whilst Ivanov (1949) has shown that inhalation of the spores of this smut led to extensive outbreaks of pneumonia in cattle in Bulgaria. The animals in these outbreaks had emphysema of the lungs with nodule formation, each focus being centred on a single spore or group of spores surrounded by asteroid projections together with histiocytes, giant cells and peripheral fibrosis. In contrast allergic reaction appeared to be responsible for a curious case of skin trouble in a farmer who had slept in a corn field where much of the crop was infected with smut, (Preininger, 1937), and actual pathogenicity by U. maydis was shown by Moore et al. (1946) to have occurred by the presence in the central nervous system of a man, who died after showing chronic nervous symptoms, of the budding yeast-like phase of the fungus. Experimental work has been carried out on rats by Tichomirov & Bogdanovic (1941). Bunt of wheat (Tilletia caries) has also been held responsible for the poisoning of dogs by Greig (1924). The three animals affected had convulsions and in one of these there was marked cerebral meningitis with spores actually present in the brain and other organs. The trouble was thought to have originated from the ingestion of food containing the spores. However when Dobson (1926) tried to confirm these observations by experimental feeding with large quantities of bunt spores, he was unable to find any deleterious effect on dogs, guinea-pigs, rabbits or fowls.

Unidentified Species of Fungi. The toxicoses included under this heading may possibly be due to the presence of some of the fungi already mentioned but in most cases the connexion with mouldy feedingstuffs is largely circumstantial and no further investigation of outbreaks has been made. The category is therefore rather unsatisfactory and the symptoms described may well be due to unrelated causes such as infectious or other diseases not recognized at the time.

Cornstalk Disease – First noticed by Mayo (1891), the effect of feeding mouldy cornstalks (maize) to horses was shown experimentally by Butler (1902) to be a leucoencephalitis or acute haemorrhagic encephalitis (Buckley & MacCallum, 1901). Further attention was directed to the condition after extensive outbreaks, again in the U. S. A., in 1934 as described by Graham (1936) and several references to the disease have appeared since that time. Generally nervous symptoms appear some four weeks after feeding has commenced and consist of staggering, lethargy and sometimes paralysis followed by death in 6-7 weeks. Post-mortem findings include softening and liquefaction of the brain and haemorrhage, congestion of the liver and swelling of the kidneys (Schwarte et al., 1937; Biester et al., 1940). Experimental feeding of mouldy corn-stalks has confirmed their toxicity but as yet no specific fungi have been isolated from them. Various attempts to demonstrate the presence of the virus of equine encephalomyelitis in the brains of affected animals were unsuccessful.

Darnel (*Lolium temulentum*) poisoning -- The poisoning of animals by this grass, one of the best known toxic plants, may possibly not be connected in any way with fungi, but there is some evidence that fungi are intimately concerned in the toxicity of the grass. Darnel is an annual plant, at one time a common weed of cereal crops, having most probably been the "tares" of the Bible. According to Leemann (1933) it is not toxic in its early stages of growth and only the seeds contain the toxin. Support for this comes from the majority of outbreaks of suspected darnel poisoning having been reported after hay containing the seeds had been fed or, in man, after bread made from flour from contaminated grain had been consumed. Nervous disturbance is a characteristic sign with giddiness, trembling, staggering followed by convulsions, delirium and death. Post-mortem examination rarely reveals any abnormality.

The connexion of darnel poisoning with fungi is long-standing but still shrouded in uncertainty. *Lolium temulentum* seeds usually contain a symbiotic fungus outside the aleurone layer but a certain proportion are free from infection. Freeman (1902) presumed that the seeds infected by the fungus were toxic and those without were not, but this suggestion is still not confirmed.

The identity of the fungus has never been established but it seems likely that it is the endophytic one known to be present in several species of *Lolium* and which does not seem to have any adverse effect on the vigour or palatability of the grass (Neill, 1952). In addition to this organism however there is an ascomycete parasitic on rye-grasses (*Gloeotinia temulentum*, syn. *Phialea temulentum*) which causes so-called "blind seed disease" and infects the inflorescences in a similar way to ergot (*Claviceps purpurea*). The ovary is replaced by a mass of hyphae and the imperfect spores (*Endoconidium temulentum*) are formed on the outside of this mass (Sampson & Western, 1954). Whether or not this fungus is the endophyte of *Lolium temulentum* is still not clear (Neill, 1941).

Mouldy hay poisoning -- The feeding of mouldy oat hay to cattle was thought by Newsom et al. (1937) to cause trembling, staggering and cyanosis of the lips leading eventually to death. The following year Thorp (1938) made further observations on the condition by experimentally feeding cattle with mouldy hay from the top and middle of a stack. The former group of animals died with typical symptoms whilst the latter were not affected, the hay from this part of the stack being of much better quality. Changes reminiscent of hydrocyanic acid poisoning were seen on post-mortem examination. Thorp fed the same hay samples to guinea-pigs, rabbits and sheep without adverse effects.

Sweet clover poisoning -- Mouldy hay with a high content of sweet clover (Melilotus alba) has been shown to be the cause of a particular type of poisoning associated with severe haemorrhage and outbreaks of the condition in the U. S. A. have been termed "sweet clover disease". Roderick & Schalk (1931) monographed the disease in cattle after making a detailed study of field and experimental cases. The earliest sign of the trouble following the feeding of mouldy hay was a delay in coagulation time of the blood which occurred at about 15 days. Internal haemorrhage was found at about three weeks and death either occurred suddenly or followed progressive weakening and took place at about 30 days. Post-mortem examination revealed extensive haemorrhages in different parts of the body, chiefly in the thoracic region and in the serosa of the rumen, but also intramuscularly. Toxicity of the hay for sheep and rabbits was demonstrated but horses were not found to be susceptible.

Roderick and Schalk were not successful in their many attempts to extract and identify the toxic substance but subsequent work on the disease by Campbell, Link and others some ten years later (Campbell et al., 1940) led to the isolation, identification and synthesis of the haemorrhagic agent as dicoumarin 3,3´- methylenebis (4-hydroxycoumarin) (Stahmann et al., 1941). A later derivative was eventually developed as the rodenticide warfarin (see Garner, 1957). The fungi associated with the original outbreaks of sweet clover disease were apparently not identified.

Vulvovaginitis in pigs — The first reports of vulvovaginitis in sows associated with the feeding of mouldy maize were made by Buxton (1927) and McNutt et al. (1928) in Iowa, involving maize harvested during the very wet autumn of 1926. The condition at first resembled normal oestral changes but occurred in piglets from six weeks to four months of age in which the vulva swelled considerably with occasional vaginal prolapse. Experimental feeding of the same mouldy maize resulted in similar symptoms within six days. Ten years later Pullar & Lerew (1937) described an almost identical outbreak in Victoria (Australia) also with maize harvested after heavy rain, and another report came from the U. S. A. in 1945 when Koen & Smith noted enlargement of the prepuce and mammary glands of castrated male piglets as an additional sign. The only other similar outbreaks recorded are those of McErlean (1952) in Ireland, but here the food was mouldy barley. The symptoms noted in these outbreaks indicate that the toxic substances were oestrogenic and therefore probably different from any of those already mentioned. In each outbreak the withdrawal of the mouldy food resulted in great improvement and eventual recovery.

Poisoning by larger fungi

Compared with the vast literature on mushroom and toadstool (the gill-fungi or agarics — Basidiomycetes) poisoning in man, there is little information even on the effect of the more deadly of these fungi on animals. Rabbits for instance have been said to be immune to the effects of the toxin of the Death Cap (Amanita phalloides) and this had led to the use of their stomach contents (chopped up with sugar or jam) as an antidote for human cases. In his invaluable book on these fungi Ramsbottom (1953) points out that rabbits will succumb to *Amanita phalloides* if it is eaten in reasonable quantities. Other poisonous species may also frequently be found in a partly eaten condition, obviously grazed by small rodents, slugs etc. Of the species thought to have been involved in outbreaks of poisoning in animals *Amanita verna* was incriminated by Piercy *et al.* (1944) in cases of severe intestinal disturbance in which two cows died following convulsions. Pieces of the fruit bodies of the fungus were found in the stomach of one animal. *Russula emetica*, an attractive bright red species, was thought to have been involved in the death of a reindeer bull in Scotland by Utsi (1956). Two extremely interesting cases of poisoning due to the morel (*Morchella esculenta*, an ascomycete) were described by Herms (1950) in two pet dogs in Germany. One of these animals had been allowed to drink the water in which a gathering of these fungi had been cooked and some hours later had attacks of vomiting, shivering, diarrhoea and haematuria whilst the other simply ate a few pieces of the cooked fungus. Both animals recovered quickly. This record seems to confirm the observation that it is not desirable to use the cooking water of morels which are otherwise considered edible.

Miscellaneous conditions

It is not possible in this review to cover all the literature on mycotoxicoses but there are a number of further instances of suspected poisoning of livestock with mouldy food which deserve a brief mention. Among these Forgacs & Carll (1955) have suggested, in a preliminary note, that more attention might be paid to fungi as a cause of haemorrhagic disease in poultry, for they were able to reproduce the field condition by feeding grain artificially infected with various species of *Aspergillus*, *Penicillium* and *Alternaria*. Eckles *et al.* (1924) investigated the significance of moulds in silage but considered that the evidence for poisoning was inconclusive, although they still advised against the feeding of badly moulded samples. Contrary to most other workers, Borchers & Peltier (1947) fed 10% of artificially moulded starter ration to chicks and actually found an improved growth rate over the controls, possibly foreshadowing the widespread present-day inclusion of antibiotics in feedingstuffs. However the fungi used were not specified and it is unlikely they included any toxin-producing strains.

List of fungi known to produce substances toxic to animals

Amanita verna Fr.

Aspergillus chevalieri (Mangin) Thom & Church
" *clavatus* Desm.
" *flavus* Link
" *fumigatus* Fresen.
" *nidulans* (Eidam) Wint.
" *niger* van Tieghem

Claviceps paspali Stev. & Hall
" purpurea (Fr.) Tul.

Dendrodochium toxicum Pidoplichko & Bilai

Diplodia zeae (Schw.) Lév.

Fusarium graminearum Schwabe (syn. F. roseum Link ex Fr.)
— imperfect state of Gibberella zeae (Schw.) Petch
(syn. G. saubinetii (Mont.) Sacc.)
" moniliforme Sheld. var. subglutinans Wollenw. & Reinking
" sporotrichioides Sherb. var. toxica Sarkisov & Kvashnina and
var. minus Wollenw.

Morchella esculenta L.

Penicillium rubrum Stoll
" urticae Bainier series

Puccinia graminis Pers.

Stachybotrys alternans Bon. var. jateli Pidoplichko

Tilletia caries DC. (syn. T. tritici (Bjerk.) Wint.)

Ustilago maydis (DC.) Tul. (syn. U. zeae (Beckm.) Unger)

Chapter 17

ERGOTISM

Ergot, 'the sclerotium of the fungus, *Claviceps purpurea* Tulasne (Fam. Hypocreaceae), developed in the ovary of the rye, *Secale cereale* L. (Fam. Gramineae)' according to the *British Pharmaceutical Codex*, 1954, p. 279, has been well known since the sixteenth century as a valuable drug in human medicine. At one time administered to hasten labour ergot is now used almost exclusively post-partum to reduce the risk of post-partum haemorrhage. Ergotism, poisoning by the ingestion of ergot, has an even longer history. There many references from the eleventh century onwards to outbreaks in western Europe of 'St. Anthony's Fire' which is now known to have been gangrenous ergotism. Ergot has been used to a more limited extent in veterinary medicine but there are many records of ergotism in cattle and other animals.

The literature on ergot and ergotism is very extensive. Three most valuable and well-documented reviews are those by Atanasoff (1920), Rozhdestvenskii (1927) and, particularly, the monograph by Barger (1931) which is still the standard source book on historical and general aspects of the effects of ergot on man. The brief review by Sampson & Western (1954, pp. 30–33) provides a convenient and concise summary of the biological aspects of ergot for mycologists.

Life Cycle of the Ergot Fungus. The sclerotia of *Claviceps purpurea* overwinter on the soil and in the spring germinate and produce ascospores which infect the flowers of cereals and grasses. An early result of infection is the production of large numbers of asexual spores (conidia) in a sticky liquid or 'honey dew' which attracts insects by which the spores are disseminated and the infection spread. The weather during these critical phases of the life-cycle has a major effect in determining the incidence of ergotized grasses in any year. Later the ovary of the host is replaced by a horn-shaped, compact mass of fungal tissue (a sclerotium) which is at first pale in colour and later purplish-brown to black. The sclerotia vary in size from 2 cm. or more in length on rye to 2 mm. on *Agrostis*.

Many cereals and grasses are susceptible to infection. The classical host is rye. Wheat is rarely attacked. Among the long list of grasses on which ergots have been recorded in Britain, perennial rye grass (*Lolium*), cocksfoot (*Dactylis*), and couch grass (*Agropyron*) are frequently heavily infected.

While there are undoubtedly a number of physiologic races of the ergot fungus with different host ranges, the current taxonomic opinion seems to be that they should, in Britain at least, all be classified as *C. purpurea*.

Among a number of other species of *Claviceps* which have been described from other parts of the world, but of which the life cycle is basically the same as that of *C. purpurea*, *C. paspali* which attacks grasses of the genus *Paspalum* may be mentioned as an economically important cause of ergotism in cattle, sheep, and horses (see Paspalum staggers, below).

Chemistry of Ergot. The active principle of ergot is a series of six isomeric pairs of alkaloids, the more important of them pharmacologically being ergotoxine and ergotamine; for details, reference may be made to the British Pharmaceutical Codex and to Barger (1931). The alkaloidal content of commercial ergot of rye varies with the source from 0.2–0.25% for Spanish ergot to 0.01–0.1% for Russian and Polish.

Symptomatology. There are two general types of ergotism in man – the convulsive and the gangrenous. Both types occur in animals but the gangrenous form is the more general.

In animals poisoning is usually chronic rather than acute. Affected animals show lameness, gangrene of the extremities of the limbs, of the end of the tail, of the tips of the ears, and of the lips, and tongue. An indented necrotic ring may develop below the hock or knee, the hind legs being more usually affected. The distal portion becomes gangrenous and is eventually shed without loss of blood. There is sometimes irritation of the digestive tract accompanied by diarrhoea and lesions in the mouth, and occasionally paralysis.

Abortion – Since statements such as "abortion is known to occur", "abortion is one of the symptoms", are not infrequently made in discussions of ergotism in livestock, it has been thought useful to examine any evidence that can be found in the literature dealing either with field outbreaks or experimental studies.

One of the most useful pharmacological actions of ergot is its ability to cause contraction of the uterine muscle, but it should be borne in mind that this action is much more marked at parturition than at any other time. It is used in midwifery, not to hasten labour, but to reduce the risk of post-partum haemorrhage. It is possibly the use of the drug in midwifery that accounts for ergot being sometimes suspected when outbreaks of abortion occur in cattle. A recent example occurred in Rhodesia. Widespread abortions were occurring in cattle and sheep at a time when ergot infestation of the veld grasses was abundant. Ergot was suspected at first but it was later shown that the Rift Valley Fever and Wesselsbron viruses were responsible (Mackinnon, 1956).

The evidence in the literature lends little support to the view that ergot causes abortion in livestock. For example Cunningham, McIntosh & Swan (1944) fed ergot to three cows and produced the clinical symptoms of gangrene of the extremities but make no mention of abortion having occurred. The cows were milking cows but it is not stated whether they were in-calf or not. Dring (1955) investigated a severe outbreak of ergotism in a herd of 43 cows and heifers in Leicestershire in which 16 of the animals had severe gangrene of the extremities, seven of them so badly as to necessitate slaughter. He stressed the fact that although 30 of them were in-calf none aborted. He also stated that 12 in-pig sows which had access to the ergot infected pastures all farrowed normally, but that two of them suffered from agalactia. Menzies (1958) studied another severe outbreak in a herd of 32 cows pastured on the banks of the river Severn. The symptoms were severe lameness and gangrene of the extremities; nine were so badly affected as to necessitate slaughter. Menzies comments that although many of the cows were in-calf none of them aborted. Forsyth (1954) noted ergot poisoning in pregnant cows and in a sow all of which carried their young to full term.

Nordskog & Clark (1945) fed ergot to pregnant sows, rats and guinea-pigs but did not produce abortion in any of these species. The striking feature in the sows was failure of development of the mammary gland with consequent agalactia. The piglets were born alive but many were smaller than normal and died from starvation as a result of the agalactia in the sows. Rats fed ergot in the earlier stages of pregnancy failed to produce any young and it was thought that foetal resorption had occurred. The guinea-pigs gave birth to normal young at term and did not develop agalactia. Nordskog (1946) and Sommer & Buchanan (1955) confirmed these findings in rats.

Nordskog (1946) also reports feeding ergot to four pregnant ewes for 50 days before lambing. All four gave birth to normal lambs and had normal milk secretion. Cunningham, Swan & Hopkirk (1944) fed ergot to 18 sheep and produced inflammation and ulceration of the alimentary tract but make no mention of abortion. Unfortunately the sex of the experimental sheep is not stated.

Osborne (1949) investigated an outbreak of abortion in a flock of 120 pedigree ewes. Over a period of nine days 41 aborted. The first abortion occurred five days after commencing to feed a mixture of rye-grass seed, clover seed and sugar beet pulp; the rye-grass seed was heavily contaminated with ergot. The circumstances pointed to a possible connexion with the feeding of the ergotized rye-grass seed. This outbreak had many of the features of an outbreak of ovine virus abortion, but it occurred before that disease had been studied and elucidated by Stamp and his colleagues.

It would therefore appear that abortion is seldom a symptom of ergot poisoning in livestock.

Cattle. Ergotism in cattle has been recorded for more than a century but the evidence for the implication of ergot has not always been very satisfactory. An authentic outbreak in Britain was described by Jones (1953) and Edwards (1953) who cite other recent reports. Further references are given by Forsyth (1954), Sampson & Western (1954), Barger (1931), and Atanasoff (1920). According to Cunningham, McIntosh & Swan (1944) milk and meat from ergotized cattle is non-toxic.

Horses. There is little really authentic information on the condition in horses, which suggests that if it does occur it cannot be common. Kaufmann (1908) fed 10 horses with 2.5 g. ergot daily for 45 days without producing any harmful effects. Long (1924) cites a paper published by Chesland, V. K. & Wilson, E. V. in Montana in 1901 in which death is stated to have occurred in horses in from 6–8 hours after eating ergotized hay.

S h e e p. Cunningham, Swan & Hopkirk (1944) have reported from New Zealand that sheep experimentally fed on perennial rye-grass infected by ergot developed ulceration and inflammation of the mucosa of the alimentary tract and, in a few cases, of the tip of the tongue but concluded that ergot poisoning in sheep does not present a sufficiently characteristic picture to permit a diagnosis on the basis of symptoms alone. They noted that none of the sheep developed gangrene of the extremities although cattle fed on the same samples of ergot did.

P i g s are apparently more resistant to ergot poisoning. Cunningham, McIntosh & Swan (1944) failed to produce any marked symptoms or lesions in two pigs by feeding massive doses of a sample of ergot which caused severe poisoning in cows. Nordskog & Clark (1945) fed nine pregnant sows experimentally with ergot and report agalactia as the only prominent finding; some of the piglets born to the experimental sows were small and weakly. Dring (1955) reported that none of 12 pregnant sows having access to a heavily ergotized pasture which produced severe poisoning in cows showed any symptoms. They all farrowed normally, but two of them had agalactia.

F o w l s are susceptible and when fed experimentally develop cyanosis and necrosis of the comb and this effect has been used as a method of assay of ergot samples.

Epidemiology and Control. There is no satisfactory treatment for ergotism other than removal of the source of the ergot. As ergots develop only in the seeding grasses, keeping pastures well grazed during the summer (or a late summer mowing) ensures that relatively few infected inflorescences are produced even in years favourable to the fungus.

Paspalum Staggers

This condition occurs in cattle, sheep or horses, grazing grasses of the genus *Paspalum* attacked by *Claviceps paspali*, and merits special notice as it differs somewhat from classical ergotism caused by *C. purpurea*.

The life cycle of *C. paspali* as described by Brown (1916) is similar to that of *C. purpurea*; the geographical range covers North and South America, Africa, Australasia and Russia. There are records of stock being poisoned in the U.S.A. (Brown & Ranck, 1915; Simpson & West, 1952), Australia (Maunder, 1936 (Queensland); Hindmarsh & Hart, 1937 (New South Wales); Grayson, 1941 (Victoria)), New Zealand (Hopkirk, 1936), Portugal (Frazão, 1955), Russia (Sarkisov, 1954), and S. Africa (Mitchell, 1918b).

The symptoms as described and illustrated by Hopkirk (1936) differ from classical ergotism in being predominantly nervous. Cows and bullocks developed a trembling of the muscles and if moved showed definite ataxia. When the animals were frightened and attempted to run the incoordinated movement resulted in their falling over in curious attitudes. Death only occurred through accident and the animals recovered on being fed healthy hay. There is some evidence that the typical ataxic symptoms of paspalum staggers are produced by infected Paspalum before the development of sclerotia. Mature sclerotia are said to induce a rather different effect with violent trembling of muscles but without ataxia. Abortion has not been reported.

Sheep poisoned with C. paspali exhibit nervous symptoms (Hindmarsh & Hart, 1937; Sarkisov, 1954) whereas when C. purpurea is involved the predominant symptoms are those of enteritis (Cunningham et al., 1944).

The symptoms in horses resemble those seen in cattle and sheep (Sarkisov, 1954).

Fescue Lameness

A condition characterized by lameness and gangrene and sloughing of the extremities occurs in cattle, but not in horses, grazing tall fescue grass (Festuca elatior) in New Zealand (Cunningham et al., 1944) and also in the U.S.A. Although the clinical appearances are identical with the gangrenous form of ergotism the outbreaks have occurred when the grass was not in the seeding stage and when no ergot could be found on it. The aetiology of this condition is obscure; it is mentioned here since it could readily be mistaken for ergotism.

BIBLIOGRAPHY

ADAMS, L., SALVIN, S. B. & HADLOW, W. J. (1956). Ringworm in a population of snowshoe hares. J. Mammal. 37, 94-99.

AINSWORTH, G.C. & AUSTWICK, P.K.C. (1954). Report to the Agricultural Research Council on a Survey of Animal Mycoses. 1952-53. Unpublished. Exeter. pp. 30.

AINSWORTH, G. C. & AUSTWICK, P. K. C. (1955a). A survey of animal mycoses in Britain: General aspects. Vet. Rec. 67, 88-97.

AINSWORTH, G. C. & AUSTWICK, P. K. C. (1955b). A survey of animal mycosis in Britain: Mycological aspects. Trans. Brit. mycol. Soc. 38, 369-386.

AINSWORTH, G. C. & GEORG, L. K. (1954). Nomenclature of the faviform Trichophytons. Mycologia 46, 9-11.

AINSWORTH, G.C. & REWELL, R.E. (1949). The incidence of aspergillosis in captive wild birds. J. comp. Path. 59, 213-224.

AKÜN, R. S. (1950). Histoplasmosis in a cat. J. Amer. vet. med. Ass. 117, 43-44.

ALBISTON, H. E. (1933). Mycotic dermatitis in the calf. Aust. vet. J. 9, 107-109.

ALBISTON, H. E. & GORRIE, C. J. R. (1935). A preliminary note on bovine nasal granuloma in Victoria. Aust. vet. J. 11, 72-76.

ALBORNOZ, J. E. (1945). Primer caso de sporotricosis equina comprobada en el país. Rev. Fac. Med. vet., Bogota 14, 33-42.

de ALMEIDA, F., da SILVA, A. C., BRANDÃO, C. H., MONTEIRO, E. L. & MOURA, R. A. (1950). Saprofitismo do Microsporum canis en gatos. Rev. Inst. Lutz 10, 49-52, 2 figs.

ANDERSEN, C. W. (1927). Tilfaelde af aspergillose hos lam. K. VetHøjsk. Aarsskr. 1927, 67-72.

ANDERSEN, J.B. & JØRGENSEN, K.L. (1949). Gaerceller (torulaceae) som årsag til mastitis efter penicillinbehandling. Nord. VetMed. 1, 958-966.

ANSBACHER, S. (1954). Treatment of actinomycosis with isoniazid. Vet. Med. 49, 357-358.

ARMFIELD, J. M. (1918). A few diseases affecting animals in Northern Rhodesia. Vet. Rec. 30, 272-278.

ASHBURN, L. L. & EMMONS, C. W. (1945). Experimental Haplosporangium infection. Arch. Path. 39, 3-8.

ASHWORTH, J. H. (1923). On Rhinosporidium seeberi (Wernicke, 1903), with special reference to its sporulation and affinities. Trans. roy. Soc. Edinb. 53, 301-342.

ASTHANA, R. P. (1944). Aspergillosis in fowls. Proc. Indian Acad. Sci. 20, Sect. B, 43-47.

ATANASOFF, D. (1920). Ergot of grains and grasses. pp. 127 [305 refs.] [Mimeographed. Issued by the Office of Cereal Investigations, Bureau of Plant Industry, U. S. Dep. Agric.]

AUSTWICK, P. K. C. (1954). The isolation of Trichophyton discoides from cattle. Vet. Rec. 66, 224-225.

AUSTWICK, P.K.C. (1958). Cutaneous streptothricosis, mycotic dermatitis and strawberry foot rot and the genus Dermatophilus Van Saceghem. Vet. Rev. Annot. 4, 33-48.

AUSTWICK. P. K. C. & VENN, J. A. J. (1957). Routine investigations into mycotic abortion. Vet. Rec. 69, 488-491.

AWROROW, A. A. (1932). Ein Fall von Nierenaktinomykose beim Rindvieh. Berl. tierärztl. Wschr. 48, 434-435.

AYYAR, V. K. (1932). Rhinosporidiosis in equines. Indian J. vet. Sci. 2, 49-52.

BABIĆ, I. (1930). Aspergiloza kao uzrok ugimica penadi roko Kastracije. Jugosl. vet. Glasn. 10, 90-92.

BAKER, A. Z., COURTENAY-DUNN, J. & WRIGHT, M. D. (1934). Observations in fungal pneumonia in the domestic fowl. Vet. J. 90, 385-389.

BAKER, E. E., MRAK, E. M. & SMITH, C. E. (1943). The morphology, taxonomy, and distribution of Coccidioides immitis Rixford and Gilchrist, 1896. Farlowia 1, 199-244.

BAKER, N. F. & DAVIS, D. W (1954). Spray application for the treatment of ringworm in cattle. Vet. Med. 49, 275-276.

BAKER, R. D. (1947). Experimental sporotrichosis in mice. Amer. J. trop. Med. 27, 749-769.

BAKER, R. D. (1947). Mucormycosis – a new disease? J. Amer. med. Ass. 163, 805-808.

BAKERSPIGEL, A. (1956). Haplosporangium in Saskatchewan rodents. Mycologia 48, 568-572.

BALLARINI, G. (1955). Aspergillus fumigatus e Rhizopus equinus in feti da aborto bovino. Nuova Vet. 31, 78-85; 117-126.

BALOZET, L. & PERNOT, P. (1936). Méningite du chien causée par un actinomyces. Bull. Acad. vét. Fr. 9, 168-175. Discussion pp. 176-177.

BARDELLI, P. & ADEMOLLO, A. (1927). Sulla resistenza delle colture di 'Criptococcus farcinimosus' Rivolta agli agenti fisici e chimici. Ann. Igiene (sper.) 37, 81-85.

BARDELLI, P. & CILLI, V. (1931). Osteo-mielite tibiale primitva di origine centrale da 'Cryptococcus farcinimosus Rivoltae'. Clin. Vet. Milano 54, 1-4.

BARGER, G. (1931). Ergot and Ergotism pp. 279. London: Gurney & Jackson. Edinburgh: Oliver & Boyd.

BARRON, C. N. (1955). Cryptococcosis in animals. J. Amer. vet. med. Ass. 127, 125-132.

BARTOLUCCI. (1903). (Cited by Del Giudice, 1956).

BATTE, E.G., & MILLER, W.S. (1953). Ringworm of horses and its control. J. Amer. vet. med. Ass. 123, 111-114.

BAUDET, E.-A.-R.-F. (1930a). Sur une teigne trichophytique du dromadaire produite par une espèce nouvelle de Grubyella, G. langeroni n. sp. Ann. Parasit. hum. comp. 8, 411-418.

BAUDET, E.-A.-R.-F. (1930b). Sur une souche d'Aleurisma lugdunense isolée de la peau d'un dromadaire. Ann. Parasit. hum. comp. 8, 628-637.

BAUDET, E.-A.-R.-F. (1932). Mucor pusillus Lindt als oorzaak van mycose bij het varken. Tijdschr. Diergeneesk. 59, 1163-1164.

BAUDET, E.-A.-R.-F. (1940). Sur une dermatomycose du chien produite par Microsporum (Achorion) gallinae. Ann. Parasit. hum. comp. 17, 443-446.

BAUER, H., FLANAGAN, J. F. & SHELDON, W. H. (1955). Experimental cerebral mucormycosis in rabbits with alloxan diabetes. Yale J. Biol. Med. 28, 29-36.

BEATON, W. G. (1928). Rep. vet. Dep. N. Nigeria, 1927, 29-31.

BEAVER, D. C. (1921). A case of actinomycosis of the omentum. Cornell Vet. 11, 217-220.

BECK, M. D. (1929). Occurrence of Coccidioides immitis in lesions of slaughtered animals. Proc. Soc. exp. Biol., N. Y. 26, 534-536.

BEKKER, J. G. (1928). Undescribed skin diseases of sheep in South Africa. J. S. Afr. vet. med. Ass. 1, No. 2. pp. 51-57.

BENBROOK, E. A., BRYANT, J. B. & SAUNDERS, L. Z. (1948). A case of blastomycosis in the horse. J. Amer. vet. med. Ass. 112, 475-478.

BENDIXEN, H. C. (1926). General Mykose hos en Ko. Maanedsskr. Dyrlaeg. 38, 369-391.

BENDIXEN, H. C. (1928). Nogle Iagttagelser vedrørende eksperimental Mykose hos Kvaeg. In "Festskrift til Bernhard Bang 1848 – 7. Juni 1928" pp. 145-171. Copenhagen: Kandrup & Wunsch Bogtrykkeri.

BENDIXEN, H. C. & PLUM, N. (1929). Schimmelpilze (Aspergillus fumigatus und Absidia ramosa) als Abortusursache beim Rinde. Acta path. microbiol. scand. 6, 252-322.

BENHAM, R. W. (1955a). Cryptococcus neoformans: "an ascomycete". Proc. Soc. exp. Biol., N. Y. 89, 243-245.

BENHAM, R. W. (1955b). The genus Cryptococcus: the present status and criteria for the identification of species. Trans. N. Y. Acad. Sci., Ser. II, 17, 418-429.

BENHAM, R. W. & KESTEN, B. (1932). Sporotrichosis: its transmission to plants and animals. J. infect. Dis. 50, 437-458.

BENITO-TRUJILLO, BORREL, A.-J. & OGER, C. (1955). Sur la présence de levures dans des laits pathologiques. Rev. méd. vét, 106, 586-592.

BENNETT, S. C. J. (1931). Cryptococcus pneumonia in Equidae. J. comp. Path. 44, 85-105.

BERG, J. (1898-99). Lungenmykose hos Svin. Maanedsskr. Dyrlaeg., 10, 33-36.

BERGNER, K. (1942). Mikrosporon equinum und Achorion gypseum als Erreger von Flechtenerkrankungen bei Pferden. Z. InfektKr. Haustiere 58, 121-141.

BEST, J. H. B. (1928). Rep. vet. Dep. N. Nigeria, 1927, 52.

de BEURMANN, [H.] & GOUGEROT, [L.] (1912). Les sporotrichoses. pp. 852. Paris: Libraire Félix Alcan.

BEVERIDGE, W. I. B. (1934). A study of twelve strains of Bacillus necrophorus, with observations on the oxygen intolerance of the organism. J. Path. Bact. 38, 467-491.

BIEBERDORF, F. W. (1953). Actinomycosis of a bovine testis. J. Amer. vet. med. Ass. 122, 49-50.

BIESTER, H. E., SCHWARTE, L. H. & REDDY, C. H. (1940). Further studies on moldy corn poisoning (leucoencephalomalacia) in horses. Vet. Med. 35, 636-639.

BISHOP, L. M. & FENSTERMACHER, R. (1933). An acid-fast actinomyces obtained from lesions resembling bovine tuberculosis. Cornell Vet. 23, 288-296.

BIZARD & POMMAY (1887). Mycose de l'autruche. Bull. Soc. cent. Méd. vét. 41, 296-302.

BLAKE, W. P. (1954). A report of two canine cases of nocardiosis in Missouri. J. Amer. vet. med. Ass. 125, 467-468.

BLANK, F. (1953). Ringworm in cattle due to Trichophyton discoides and its transmission to man. Canad. J. comp. Med. 17, 277-281.

BLANK, F. (1955). Dermatophytes of animal origin transmissible to man. Amer. J. med. Sci. 229, 302-316.

BLANK, F. (1957a). Favus of mice. Canad. J. Microbiol. 3, 885-896.

BLANK, F. (1957b). (Personal communication.)
BLANK, F., BYRNE, J.L., PLUMMER, P.J.G. & AVERY, R.J. (1953). Isolation of Trichophyton granulosum Sabouraud, 1909, from chinchillas showing "fur-slipping". Canad. J. comp. Med. 17, 396-402.
BLANK, F. & CRAIG, G.E. (1954). Family epidemics of ringworm contracted from cattle. Canad. med. Ass. J. 71, 234-235.
BLAXLAND, J. D. (1951). The causes of epidemic outbreaks of moniliasis in turkeys. Off. Rep. IXth World's Poult. Congr., Paris 3, 21-27.
BLAXLAND, J.D. & FINCHAM, I.H. (1950). Mycosis of the crop (moniliasis) in poultry, with particular reference to serious mortality occurring in young turkeys. Brit. vet. J. 106, 221-231.
BLAXLAND, J. D. & MARKSON, L. M. (1954). Observations on the transmissibility and pathogenesis of moniliasis in turkey poults. Brit. vet. J. 110, 139-145.
BLOCH, A. (1870). Beiträge zur Kenntnis der Pilzbildung in den Geweben des tierischen Organismus. Thesis, Stettin (Greifswald) pp. 36. (Cited by Urbain & Guillot, 1938.)
BODIN, E. & LENORMAND. C. (1912). Recherches sur les poisons produits par l'Aspergillus fumigatus. Ann. Inst. Pasteur 26, 371-380.
BØE, J., HARTMANN, O. & THJØTTA, T. (1939). A serological study of Aspergillus fumigatus. Acta path. microbiol. scand. 16, 178-186.
BOHL, E.H., JONES, D.O., FARRELL, R.L., CHAMBERLAIN, D.M., COLE, C.R. & FERGUSON, L. C. (1953). Nocardiosis in the dog. A case report. J. Amer. vet. med. Ass. 122, 81-85.
BOLLINGER, O. (1880). Ueber Pilzkrankheiten höher und niederer Thiere. Ärztl. Intelligenzblatt No. 9-11. (Cited by Urbain & Guillot, 1938.)
BOOTH, B. H. (1952). Mouse ringworm. Arch. Derm. Syph., Chicago 66, 65-69.
BORCHERS, R. & PELTIER, G. L. (1947). Molded foodstuffs. I. Supplementary value in chick starting rations. Poult. Sci. 26, 194-197.
BORKOWSKA-TRIPPENBACH, B. & SZWEJKOWSKI, H. (1950). Moniliasis u drobiu. Proc. 2nd. Meet. Polish Parasitol. Soc. pp. 105-106.
BOURNAY, J. (1895). Pneumonomycose aspergillain chez une vache. Rev. vét. Toulouse 20, 121-128.
BRESLAU, A.M. (1955). Comparative histochemical studies on Coccidioides immitis and Haplosporangium parvum. J. Histochem. Cytochem. 3, 141-147.
BROCQ-ROUSSEU, D., URBAIN, A. & BAROTTE, J. (1927). Étude des teignes du cheval et de l'immunité dans les teignes expérimentales. Ann. Inst. Pasteur 41, 513-553.
BROOKSBANK, N. H. & AUSTWICK, P. K. C. (1955). Susceptibility of inbred and outbred chicks to aspergillosis. Brit. vet. J. 111, 64-67.
BROWN, H. B. (1916). Life history and poisonous properties of Claviceps paspali. J. agric. Res. 7, 401-406.
BROWN, H. B. & RANCK, E. M. (1915). Forage poisoning due to Claviceps paspali in Paspalum. Bull. Miss. agric. Exp. Sta. No. 6. pp. 35, 18 figs.
BRUERE, A. N. (1955). Actinomycosis of the digestive tract in cattle. N. Z. vet. J. 3, 121-122.
BRUMPT, E. (1927). Précis de Parasitologie. 4th Edit. Vol. 1, Paris: Masson et cie:
BUCK, G. (1948). Actinomycose ou streptothricose cutanée des bovins à Madagascar (Drodro, Boka). Bull. Off. int. Epiz. 29, 117-121.
BUCKLEY, S.S. & MacCALLUM, W.G. (1901). Acute hemorrhagic encephal-

itis prevalent among horses in Maryland. Amer.vet. Rev.25, 99-102. (Cited by Schwarte et al., 1937.)
BUENO, P. & FARIA, P. N. (1941). Rinosporidiose em muar. Arch. Inst. biol. (Def. agric. anim.), S. Paulo 12, 297-302.
BULL, L. B. (1929). Dermatomycosis of the sheep (lumpy or matted wool) due to "Actinomyces dermatonomus" (new species). Aust. J. exp. Biol. 6, 301-314.
BULLEN, J. J. (1949). The yeast-like form of Cryptococcus farciminosus (Rivolta): (Histoplasma farciminosum). J. Path. Bact. 61, 117-120.
BULLEN, J. J. (1950-51). Epizoötic lymphangitis. J. R. Army vet. Cps. 21, 158-159; 22, 8-11.
BURGEON. (1929). A propos de trois cas d'aspergillose animale. Bull. Soc. méd.-chir. Indoch. 7, 116-121.
BURGISSER, H. (1955). Mycoses nasales chez le chevreuil. Schweiz. Arch. Tierheilk. 97, 434-438.
BURKEY, L. A., BUCKNER, C. R., UNDERWOOD, P. C. & SWETT, W. W. (1951). Trends in the incidence of mastitis infections in different organisms. U. S. Dep. Agric. BDI- Inf. 129, pp. 3.
BURNS, R. H. G. & SIMMONS, G. C. (1952). A case of actinomycotic infection in a horse. Aust. vet. J. 28, 34-35.
BURNSIDE, J. E., SIPPEL, W. L., FORGACS, J., CARLL, W. T., ATWOOD, M. B. & DOLL, E. R. (1957). A disease of swine and cattle caused by eating moldy corn. II. Experimental production with pure cultures of molds. Amer. J. vet. Res. 18, 817-824.
BUTLER, T. (1902). Notes on a feeding experiment to produce leucoencephalitis in a horse with positive results. Amer. vet. Rev. 26, 748-751. (Cited by Schwarte et al., 1937.)
BUXTON, E. A. (1927). Mycotic vaginitis in gilts. Vet. Med. 22, 428 & 451-452.
CALERO M., C. & ORTIZ O., P. (1947). Actinomycosis in a Hydrochoerus isthmius Goldman (Isthmian Capybara or Poncho). Amer. J. trop. Med. 27, 377-381.
CAMPBELL, H. A., ROBERTS, W. L., SMITH, W. K. & LINK, K. P. (1940). Studies on the hemorrhagic sweet clover disease. I. The preparation of hemorrhagic concentrates. J. biol. Chem. 136, 47-55.
CANESTRELLI, O. (1939). Contributo allo studio delle micosi interne nel cane. Nuovo Ercol. 44, 121-133.
CARINI, A. (1940). Sobre um parasito semelhante do Rhinosporidium, encontrado em quistos da pele de uma Hyla. Arch. Inst. Biol. (Def. agric. anim.), S. Paulo 11, 93-96.
CARLL, W. T., FORGACS, J. & HERRING, A. S. (1953). Toxic Aspergilli isolated from a food concentrate. Vet. Med. 48, 324 & 342.
CARLL, W. T., FORGACS, J. & HERRING, A. S. (1954). Toxicity of fungi isolated from a food concentrate. Amer. J. Hyg. 60, 8-14.
CARLL, W. T., FORGACS, J., HERRING, A. S. & MAHLANDT, B. G. (1955). Toxicity of Aspergillus fumigatus substrates to animals. Vet. Med. 50, 210-212.
CARMICHAEL, J. W. (1951). The pulmonary fungus Haplosporangium parvum. II. Strain and generic relationships. Mycologia 43, 605-624.
CARNAGHAN, R. B. A., GITTER, M. & BLAXLAND, J. D. (1956). Favus in poultry: an outbreak of Trichophyton gallinae infection. Vet. Rec. 68, 600-601.
CARTER, H.S. & YOUNG, J.L. (1950). Note on the isolation of Cryptococcus

neoformans from a sample of milk. J. Path. Bact. 62, 271-273.
CASSAMAGNAGHI, A. (1949). Tuberculosis en palomas coexistiendo con una blastomicosis del aparato digestivo. Rev. Med. vet., Montevideo 24, 925-928.
CASTELLANI, A. (1937). A preliminary report of two pathogenic fungi: Trichophyton dankaliense n. sp., and Sporotrichum anglicum n. sp. J. trop. Med. (Hyg.) 40, 313-318.
CASTELLANI, A. & STURGESS, G. W. (1905). Ann. Rep. Bact. Inst., Ceylon for the year 1904. pp. 8 and 9.
De CASTRO, A. M. (1928). Tinhas dos animaes domesticos em São Paulo. Arch. Inst. biol. (Def. agric. anim.), S. Paulo 1, 201-206.
CATANEI, A. (1925). Présence d'un Monilia sur la langue de singes d'Algérie. C. R. Soc. Biol., Paris 93, 92-94.
CATANEI, A. (1931). Étude d'une teigne de mouton produite par une espèce nouvelle de Trichophyton, T. pruinosum n. sp. Bull. Soc. Pat. exot. 24, 296-301.
CATANEI, A. (1939). Études des teignes des animaux en Algérie. Arch. Inst. Pasteur Algér. 17, 520-529.
CATANEI, A. (1942). Les teignes de la souris blanche à Algér. Arch. Inst. Pasteur Algér. 20, 305-308.
CATANEI, A. (1946). Nouvelles observations sur les teignes en Algérie et dans les colonies françaises. Arch. Inst. Pasteur Algér. 24, 116-121.
CATANEI, A. & IZAC, R. (1941). Nouvelle teigne d'origine animale observée chez un indigène algérien. Arch. Inst. Pasteur Algér. 19, 339-341.
CEDERVALL, A. (1954). Über Streptothrikose bei Karnivoren. Nord. VetMed. 6, 159-172.
CENI, C. & BESTA, C. (1902). Ueber die Toxine von Aspergillus fumigatus und flavescens und deren Beziehung zur Pellagra. Zbl. allg. Path. path. Anat. 13, 930.
CENI, C. & BESTA, C. (1905). Sclerosi in placche sperimentale da tossici aspergillari. Sulla persistenza del potere vitale e patogeno della spora aspergillare nell'organismo animale. Contributo sperimentale alla recidivita della pellagra. Arch. ital. Mal. ner. mentali 42, 125; 496. (Cited by Urbain & Guillot, 1938.)
CHARLES, V. K. (1940). A ringworm disease of muskrats transferable to man. J. Wash. Acad. Sci. 30, 338-344.
CHESTER, F. O. (1901). A manual of determinative bacteriology, pp. 401. London; Macmillan & Co.
CHICK, E. W., SUTLIFF, W. D., RAKICH, J. H. & FURCOLOW, M.L. (1956). Epidemiological aspects of cases of blastomycosis admitted to Memphis, Tennessee, hospitals during the period 1922-54: a review of 86 cases. Amer. J. med. Sci. 231, 253-262.
CHODNIK, K.S. (1956). Mycotic dermatitis of cattle in British West Africa. J. comp. Path. 66, 179-186.
CHRISTENSEN, J. J. & KERNKAMP, H. C. H. (1936). Studies on the toxicity of blighted barley to swine. Tech. Bull. Minn. Agr. Exp. Sta. No. 113, pp. 28.
CHRISTIANSEN, M. (1922). Generel Mucormykose hos Svin. K. VetHojsk. Aarsskr. 80, 133-190.
CHRISTIANSEN, M. (1929). Mucormykose beim Schwein. I. Mitteilung. Virchows Arch. 273, 829-858.
CHUTE, H. L., WITTER, J. F., ROUNTREE, J. L. & O'MEARA, D. C. (1955). The pathology of a fungous infection associated with a caponizing

injury. J. Amer. vet. med. Ass. 127, 207-209.
CILLI, V., BATTELLI, C. & CECCARELLI, A. (1954). Richerche sperimentali su di uno stipite di Asteroides (Proactinomyces, Nocardia) asteroides repertato in un caso di actinomicosi spontanea del cane. Boll. Ist. sieroter. Milano 33, 139-173.
COLLET, P. (1934). Sporotrichose gommeuse disséminée chez un jeune chien. Bull. Soc. Sci. vét. Lyon 37, 72-82.
COLLET, P., COULON, J., JOUBERT, L. & DALLERY, L. (1952-53). Nouveaux cas d'actinomycose chez le furet. Bull. Soc. Sci. vét. Lyon 54-55, 363-368.
COLLIER, W. A. & WINCKEL, W. E. F. (1952). Beiträge zur geographischen Pathologie von Suriname. 6. Histoplasmose bei Säugetieren in Suriname. Leeuwenhoek ned. Tijdschr. 18, 349-356.
CONANT, N. F. (1937). Studies in the genus Microsporum. III. Taxonomic studies. Arch. Derm. Syph., Chicago 36, 781-808.
CONANT, N. F., SMITH, D. T., BAKER, R. D., CALLAWAY, J. L. & MARTIN, D. S. (1954). Manual of clinical mycology. 2nd Edit. Philadelphia (& London): W. B. Saunders Co.
COPE, Z. (1938). Actinomycosis. pp. 248. London: Oxford University Press.
CORDY, D. R. & HOOP, J. D. (1953). Coccidioidomycosis of the skeleton in a dog. N. Amer. Vet. 34, 44-46.
COSTANTIN, J. & LUCET, A. (1903). Sur un Rhizopus pathogène. Bull. Soc. mycol. Fr. 19, 200-216.
COURTOIS, G., SÉGRETAIN, G., MARIAT, F. & LEVADITI, J.-C. (1955). Mycose cutanée à corps levuriformes observée chez des singes africains en captivité. Ann. Inst. Pasteur 89, 124-127.
COUTELEN, F. & COCHET, G. (1942). Les rongeurs domestiques, réservoirs de virus en mycopathologie humaine et vétérinaire. Ann. Parasit. hum. comp. 19, 85-95.
COX, L. B. & TOLHURST, J. C. (1946). Human torulosis: a clinical, pathological and microbiological study with a report of thirteen cases. pp. 149. Melbourne: Melbourne Univ. Press in association with Oxford Univ. Press, Melbourne & London.
CROSS, R. F., NAGAO, W. T. & MORRISON, R. H. (1953). Canine nocardiosis — a report of two cases. J. Amer. vet. med. Ass. 123, 535-536.
CUNNINGHAM, I.J., McINTOSH, I.G. & SWAN, J.B. (1944). The non-toxicity of milk and meat from ergotized cattle. N. Z. J. Sci. Tech., Sect. A. 26, 125-126.
CUNNINGHAM, I.J., SWAN, J.B. & HOPKIRK, C.S.M. (1944). The symptoms of ergot poisoning in sheep. N. Z. J. Sci. Tech., Sect. A. 26, 121-124.
CURASSON, G. (1942). Traité de pathologie exotique vétérinaire et comparée. 2nd Edit. Vol. II. Maladies microbiennes. Paris: Vigot Frères.
CURASSON, G. (1947). Le chameau et ses maladies. pp. 462. Paris: Vigot Frères.
DANBOLT, N. & MOSSIGE, K. (1939). Sølvrev som smittekilde for Trichophyti hos mennesker. Norsk. VetTidsskr. 51, 85-92.
DATTA, S. (1932). A new fungus Eidamella actoni parasitic to the dog. Indian vet. J. 8, 169-178.
DAUBNEY, R. (1927). Bovine lymphangitis, or tropical actinomycosis. J. comp. Path. 40, 195-216.
DAVIDSON, A. M., GREGORY, P. H. & BIRT, A. R. (1934). A clinical and mycological study of suppurative ringworm. Canad. med. Ass. J. 31,

587-591.
DAVIS, C. L., ANDERSON, W. A. & McCRORY, B. R. (1955). Mucormycosis in food-producing animals. A report of twelve cases. J. Amer. vet. med. Ass. 126, 261-267.
DAVIS, C. L., STILES, G. W., Jr. & McGREGOR, A. N. (1937). Pulmonary coccidioidal granuloma. A new site of infection in cattle. J. Amer. vet. med. Ass. 91, 209-215.
DAVIS, D. J. (1923). Comparative study of crypt content of tonsils of man, pig and cow, with especial reference to actinomyces-like granules. J. Amer. med. Ass. 81, 1172-1174.
DAVIS, W.A. & McCLUNG, L.S. (1940). Aspergillosis in wild herring gulls. J. Bact. 40, 321-323.
DELAMATER, E. D. (1939). The squirrel as a new host to a ringworm fungus. Mycologia 31, 519-526.
DEMPSEY, M. (1954). Some diseases causing skin lesions, and the effects on leather made from such diseased skins. Bull. epiz. Dis. Afr. 2, 269-277.
DICKE, R. J. (1953). Maggot therapy of actinomycosis. J. econ. Ent. 46, 706-707.
DOBBERSTEIN, J. (1936). Beiträge zur Pathologie des Zentralnervensystems bei Tieren. III. Leptomeningitis mykotica bei eimen Elch. Berl. tierärztl. Wschr. 52, 144-145.
DOBSON, N. (1926). The toxicity of the spores of Tilletia tritici to animals. Trans. Brit. mycol. Soc. 11, 82-91.
DODGE, C. W. (1935). Medical Mycology: fungous diseases of men and other mammals. St. Louis, U. S. A. (& London): C. V. Mosby.
DOWDING, E. S. (1947a). Haplosporangium in Canadian rodents. Mycologia 39, 372-373.
DOWDING, E. S. (1947b). The pulmonary fungus, Haplosporangium parvum, and its relationship with some human pathogens. Canad. J. Res., Sect. E. 25, 195-206.
DOZIER, H. L. (1943). Occurrence of ringworm disease and lumpy jaw in the muskrat in Maryland. J. Amer. vet. med. Ass. 102, 451-453.
DRAKE, C. H. (1948). The pathogenicity of Aspergillus nidulans. Mycopathologia 4, 103-119.
DRING, J. C. (1955). Unpublished report. [Copies available from Commonwealth Bureau of Animal Health, Weybridge, Surrey.]
ECKLES, C. H., FITCH, C. P. & SEAL, J. L. (1924). Molds in silage and their significance in the production of disease among live stock. J. Amer. vet. med. Ass. 64, 716-722.
EDINGTON, J. W. (1934). Actinomycosis in a cat. Vet. Rec. 14, 311-312.
EDWARDS, C. M. (1953). Ergot poisoning in young cattle. II. Vet. Rec. 65, 158-159.
ELDER, T. D. & BAKER, R. D. (1956). Pulmonary mucormycosis in rabbits with alloxan diabetes. Increased invasiveness of fungus during acute toxic phase of diabetes. Arch. Path. 61, 159-168.
EMMEL, M. W. (1929). Aspergillus fumigatus infection of the kidney. J. Amer. vet. med. Ass. 75, 369.
EMMONS, C. W. (1934). Dermatophytes. Natural grouping based on the form of the spores and accessory organs. Arch. Derm. Syph., Chicago 30, 337-362.
EMMONS, C. W. (1940). Trichophyton mentagrophytes (Pinoyella simii) isolated from dermatophytosis in the monkey. Mycopathologia 2,

317-319.
EMMONS, C. W. (1942). Isolation of coccidioides from soil and rodents. Publ. Hlth Rep., Wash. 57, 109-111.
EMMONS, C. W. (1943). Coccidioidomycosis in wild rodents. A method of determining the extent of endemic areas. Publ. Hlth Rep., Wash. 58, 1-5.
EMMONS, C. W. (1947). Biology of Coccidioides. In "Biology of pathogenic fungi," pp. 71-82. [Waltham, Mass.: The Chronica Botanica Co.; London: Wm. Dawson and Sons, Ltd.]
EMMONS, C. W. (1949). Isolation of Histoplasma capsulatum from soil. Publ. Hlth Rep., Wash. 64, 892-896.
EMMONS, C. W. (1951). Isolation of Cryptococcus neoformans from soil. J. Bact. 62, 685-690.
EMMONS, C. W. (1952). Cryptococcus neoformans strains from a severe outbreak of bovine mastitis. Mycopathologia 6, 231-234.
EMMONS, C. W. (1953). The natural occurrence in animals and soil of fungi which cause disease in man. Proc. VIIth int. bot. Congr., Stockholm, 1950, 416-420.
EMMONS, C.W. (1955a). Histoplasmosis. Bull. N. Y. Acad. Med. 31, 627-638.
EMMONS, C. W. (1955b). Mycoses of animals. In "Advances in veterinary science," 2, 47-63. [New York: Academic Press Inc.]
EMMONS, C. W. (1955c). Saprophytic sources of Cryptococcus neoformans associated with the pigeon (Columba livia). Amer. J. Hyg. 62, 227-232.
EMMONS, C.W. & ASHBURN, L.L. (1942). The isolation of Haplosporangium parvum n. sp. and Coccidioides immitis from wild rodents. Their relationship to coccidioidomycosis. Publ. Hlth Rep., Wash. 57, 1715-1727.
EMMONS, C. W., BELL, J. A. & OLSON, B. J. (1947). Naturally occurring histoplasmosis in Mus musculus and Rattus norvegicus. Publ. Hlth Rep., Wash. 62, 1642-1646.
EMMONS, C. W., OLSON, B. J. & ELDRIDGE, W. W. (1945). Studies on the role of fungi in pulmonary disease. I. Cross-reaction of histoplasmin. Publ. Hlth Rep., Wash. 60, 1383-1394.
EMMONS, C.W., ROWLEY, D.A., OLSON, B.J., MATTERN, C.F.T., BELL, J. A., POWELL, E. & MARCEY, E. A. (1955). Histoplasmosis. Proved occurrence of inapparent infection in dogs, cats, and other animals. Amer. J. Hyg. 61, 40-44.
ENGEL, J. A. & Van der MAAS, J. C. A. (1955). Schimmelinfectie bij een runderfoetus. Tijdschr. Diergeneesk. 80, 404-405.
ERICKSON, A. B. (1949). The fungus (Haplosporangium parvum) in the lungs of the beaver (Castor canadensis). J. Wildlife Mgmt. 13, 419-420.
ERIKSON, D. (1935). The pathogenic aerobic organisms of the actinomyces group. Spec. Rep. Ser. med. Res. Coun., Lond. No. 203, pp. 61. H.M.S.O.
ERIKSON, D. (1940). Pathogenic anaerobic organisms of the actinomyces group. Spec. Rep. Ser. med. Res. Coun., Lond. No. 240, pp. 63.
ERIKSON, D. & PORTEOUS, J. W. (1953). The cultivation of Actinomyces israelii in a progressively less complex medium. J. gen. Microbiol. 8, 464-474.
ERIKSON, D. & PORTEOUS, J. W. (1955). Commensalism in pathogenic anaerobic Actinomyces cultures. J. gen. Microbiol. 13, 261-272.
ERRINGTON, P. L. (1942). Observations on a fungus skin disease of Iowa

muskrats. Amer. J. vet. Res. 3, 195-201.

FARNESS, O. J. (1940). Coccidioidal infection in a dog. J. Amer. vet. med. Ass. 97, 263-264.

FARQUHARSON, J. (1937). Intravenous use of sodium iodide in actinomycosis. J. Amer. vet. med. Ass. 91, 551-554.

FAURE, L. (1939). Traitement des teignes du cheval par la chaleur. Ann. Parasit. hum. comp. 17, 108-110.

FAVA, A. & ZANACCA, G. (1951). Rara forma cistica di actinomicosi cardiaca in un bovino. Zooprofilassi 6, 55-65.

FEY, H., HOLM, P. & TEUSCHER, E. (1954). Nocardiosen. Kasuistische Mitteilung über einen Fall von septischer Nocardiose beim Hund und zwei Fälle von Nocardia-Abortus beim Rind. Schweiz. Arch. Tierheilk. 96, 642-648.

FLATLA, J. L. (1939). Ringorm hos rev. Skand. VetTidskr. 29, 753-780.

FLORES del F., C. H. & BRNCIC, J. D. (1948). Moniliasis renal espontanea en cuy (Cavia cobaya). Accion patogena experimental. Agric. Téc., Chile 8, 87-111.

FLORES del F., C. H., GUTIERREZ J., E. & BIEFANG, B., F. (1954). Paralelismo etiológico entre la tiña del perro y gato y la del niño en la ciudad de Santiago. Rev. vet. Milit., B. Aires 2, 213.

FØLGER, A. F. (1906-07). Et Tilfaelde af Pneumonomykose hos en Ko. Maanedsskr. Dyrlaeg. 18, 311-322.

FOLEY, G. E. & WINTER, W. D., Jr. (1949). Increased mortality following penicillin therapy of chick embryos infected with Candida albicans var. stellatoidea. J. infect. Dis. 85, 268-274.

FORD, E. J. H. (1956). Ringworm in cattle: an account of an outbreak. Vet. Rec. 68, 803-807.

FORGACS, J. & CARLL, W. T. (1955). Preliminary mycotoxic studies on hemorrhagic disease in poultry. Vet. Med. 50, 172.

FORGACS, J., CARLL, W. T., HERRING, A. S. & MARLANDT, B. G. (1954). A toxic Aspergillus clavatus isolated from feed pellets. Amer. J. Hyg. 60, 15-26.

FORSYTH, A. A. (1954). British poisonous plants. Bull. Minist. Agric., Lond. No. 161, pp. 116.

FOULERTON, A. G. R. (1899?). Section showing a mycosis (? aspergillar) of lung of horse. Trans. path. Soc. Lond. 50, 272.

FOX, H. (1923). Disease in captive wild mammals and birds; incidence, description, comparison. pp. 665. Philadelphia: Lippincott.

FRANK, A. (1890). Eine mykotische Neubildung am Widerrist des Pferdes. Wschr. Tierheilk. Viehz. 34, 13-15.

FRAZÃO, T. L. (1955). Algumas considerações sobre a embriaguez dos bovinos no vale do Sado. Bol. pecuar. 23, No. 2. pp. 29-42.

FREEMAN, E. M. (1902). The seed-fungus of Lolium temulentum L., the darnel. Proc. roy. Soc. 71, 27-30. (Cited by York, 1957.)

FRESENSIUS, G. (1850-53). Beiträge zur Mykologie 10, 81. (Cited by Urbain & Guillot, 1938.)

FRIEDBERGER & FRÖHNER. (1905). Veterinary pathology. Vol. II. [Translated by M. M. Hayes.] pp. 767. London: Hurst & Blackett.

FRIEDMAN, L., SMITH, C. E. & GORDON, L. E. (1955). The assay of virulence of coccidioides in white mice. J. infect. Dis. 97, 311-316.

FROST, B. M. (1940). A study of the actinomyces in the mouths of normal cattle. Thesis, Cornell pp. 21.

FROTHINGHAM, L. (1902). A tumor-like lesion in the lung of a horse

caused by a Blastomyces (Torula). J. med. Res. 8, 31-43.
FUENTES, C. A. & ABOULAFIA, R. (1955). T. mentagrophytes from apparently healthy guinea pigs. Arch. Derm. Syph., Chicago 71, 478-480.
FUENTES, C. A., BOSCH, Z. A. & BOUDET, C. C. (1954). Occurrence of Trichophyton mentagrophytes and Microsporum gypseum on hairs of healthy cats. J. invest. Derm. 23, 311-313.
FURCOLOW, M. L. & RUHE, J. S. (1949). Histoplasmin sensitivity among cattle. Amer. J. publ. Hlth 39, 719-721.
GALLI, G. (1954). Osservazione e studi su casi di mastite micotica bovina. Vet. ital. 5, 587-604.
GARNER, R. J. (1957). Veterinary toxicology. Formerly Lander's veterinary toxicology. pp. 415. London: Baillière, Tindall & Cox.
GENERALI, G. (1879). Di una malattia epizootica nei colombi (Micosi delle vie aerae nei colombi). Med. vet., Modena 25, 272-274.
GENTLES, J. C. & O'SULLIVAN, J. G. (1957a). The isolation of ringworm fungi from unusual hosts. Vet. Rec. 69, 132.
GENTLES, J. C. & O'SULLIVAN, J. G. (1957b). Correlation of human and animal ringworm in west of Scotland. Brit. med. J. ii, 678-682.
GEORG, L. K. (1949). Conversion of tryptophane to nicotinic acid by Trichophyton equinum. Proc. Soc. exp. Biol., N. Y. 72, 653-655.
GEORG, L. K. (1950). The relation of nutrition to the growth and morphology of Trichophyton faviforme. Mycologia 42, 693-716.
GEORG, L. K. (1952). Cultural and nutritional studies of Trichophyton gallinae and Trichophyton megnini. Mycologia 44, 470-492.
GEORG, L. K. (1954). The diagnosis of ringworm in animals. Vet. Med. 49, 157-166.
GEORG, L. K., AJELLO, L. & GORDON, M. A. (1951). A selective medium for the isolation of Coccidioides immitis. Science 114, 387-389.
GEORG, L. K., KAPLAN, W. & CAMP, L. B. (1957a). Trichophyton equinum — a re-evaluation of its taxonomic status. J. invest. Derm. 29, 27-37.
GEORG, L. K., KAPLAN, W. & CAMP, L. B. (1957b). Equine ringworm with special reference to Trichophyton equinum. Amer. J. vet. Res. 18, 798-810.
GEORG, L. K., ROBERTS, C. S., MENGES, R. W. & KAPLAN, W. (1957). Trichophyton mentagrophytes infections in dogs and cats. J. Amer. vet. med. Ass. 130, 427-432.
GIERKE, A. G. (1932). A preliminary report on a mycosis of turkeys. Mon. Bull. Calif. Dep. Agric. 21, 229-231.
GILMAN, H. L. & BIRCH, R. R. (1925). A mould associated with abortion in cattle. Cornell Vet. 15, 81-89.
GILTNER, L. T. (1918). The occurrence of coccidioidal granuloma (oidiomycosis) in cattle. J. agric. Res. 14, 533-541.
GINSBERG, A. & LITTLE, A. C. W. (1948). Actinomycosis in dogs. J. Path. Bact. 60, 563-572.
GIORDANO, A. (1940). Studio micologico del Debaryomyces neoformans (Sanfelice) Red., Cif. et Giord. e significato della specie nella patologia animale. Mycopathologia 1, 274-304.
GITTER, M. & AUSTWICK, P. K. C. (1957). The presence of fungi in abomasal ulcers of young calves: a report of seven cases. Vet. Rec. 69, 924-928.
Del GIUDICE, V. (1956). Aspergillosi polmonare in un bovino. Studio istopatologico. Atti Soc. ital. Sci. vet. 9, 393-397.
GLEISER, C. A. (1953). Mucormycosis in animals. A report of three cases.

J. Amer. vet. med. Ass. 123, 441-445.
GORET, P. & JOUBERT, L. (1951). Sur une nouvelle espèce de Streptomyces (Streptomyces galtieri n. sp.), isolée d'un cas d'actinomycose septicémique chez le chien. Ann. Parasit. hum. comp. 26, 118-127.
GOTTI. (1871). G. Anat. Fis. Path. Anim. (Cited by Lucet, 1897.)
GRAHAM, R. (1936). Cornstalk disease investigations. Toxic encephalitis or non-virus encephalomyelitis of horses. Vet. Med. 31, 46-50.
GRAWITZ, P. (1877). Beiträge zur systematischen Botanik der pflanzlichen Parasiten mit experimentellen Untersuchungen über die durch sie bedingten Krankheiten. Virchows Arch. 70, 546-598.
GRAWITZ, P. (1881). Experimentelles zur Infektionsfrage. Berl. klin. Wschr. 18, 189-192.
GRAY, D. F. & HOEBEN, J. G H. (1941). Infections of the mycetoma type in dogs. Aust. vet. J. 17, 93-101.
GRAYSON, A. R. (1941). Paspalum ergotism in cattle. J. Dep. Agric. Vict. 39, 441-442 & 446.
GREEN, H. F. (1956). A survey of skin diseases of goats in Kenya and their effect on the finished leather. J. Soc. Leath. Tr. Chem. 40, 259-264.
GREIG, J. RUSSELL (1924). Note on the association of Tilletia tritici with "epileptiform convulsions" in the dog. Trans. Brit. mycol. Soc. 10, 121-122.
GRIGORAKI, L., FAYET & MAGROU, J. (1926). Sur un nouveau dermatophyte du genre Aleurisma. C. R. Soc. Biol., Paris 95, 649-651.
GROHE. (1870). Vorhandlungen ärztliche Gesellschaften. Medizinische Verein zu Greifswald. Sitzung. von 7. August 1869. Berl. klin. Wschr. 10, 7, 8-9.
GRÜTZ, O. (1928). Sporotrichosen und verwandte Krankheiten. In Jadassohn, J. [Ed. by.]: Handbuch der Haut- und Geschlechtskrankheiten, Vol. 11, pp. 722-822. Berlin: Springer Verlag.
GUILHON, J., CHARTON, A. & DURIEUX, J. (1955). Teigne du mouton. Bull. Acad. vét. Fr. 28, 465-468.
GUILHON, J. & OBLIGI, S. (1956). Une nouvelle enzootie de teigne ovine. Bull. Acad. vét. Fr. 29, 443-445.
HAGE, T.J. & MOULTON, J. E. (1954). Skeletal coccidioidomycosis in dogs. Cornell Vet. 44, 489-500.
HAMMER, D. & ENGLERT, H. K. (1956). Torulopsisendocarditis bei einem Bullen. Tierärztl. Umsch. 11, 47-51.
HARDENBROOK, H., Jr. (1946). Studies in cowpox. III. A note on the fungal flora of bovine teat and udder lesions. Cornell Vet. 36, 251-258,
HARE, T. (1937). A study of 110 consecutive cases of disease in pigeons. Vet. Rec. 49, 680-686.
HARRISON, F. C. (1928). A systematic study of some torulae. Trans. roy. Soc. Can. Sect. V. 22, 187-225.
HARRISS, S. T. (1948). Proliferative dermatitis of the legs ("strawberry foot rot") in sheep. J. comp. Path. 58, 314-328.
HART, L. (1947). Moniliasis in turkeys and fowls in New South Wales. Aust. vet. J. 23, 191-192.
HASEGAWA, M., & YAMAMOTO, K. (1936). Über einen bei Affen gezüchteten Pilz: Microsporon fulvum. Jap. J. Derm. Urol. (Abstr. Sect.) 39, 23-25.
HAYES, F. A. (1956). Treatment of ringworm in chinchillas. J. Amer. vet. med. Ass. 128, 193-195.
HAZEN, E. L., LITTLE, G. N. & RESNICK, H. (1952). The hamster as a vehicle for the demonstration of pathogenicity of Actinomyces bovis. J. Lab.

clin. Med. 40, 914-918.
HEILMAN, F. R. (1952). Effect of stilbamidine on blastomycosis in mice. Proc. Mayo Clin. 27, 455-458.
van HELLENS, O. (1902-03). Pneumonomycosis aspergillina hos däggdjur. Maanedsskr. Dyrlaeg. 14, 512-520.
HEMMERT-HALSWICK, A. (1946). Zur Pathologie der Lymphangitis epizootica des Pferdes. Berl. Münch. tierärztl. Wschr. August, 13-15.
HENDERSON, W. W. (1927). Rep. vet. Dep. N. Nigeria, 1926, 10.
HENNING, M. W. (1956). Animal diseases in South Africa. 3rd Edit. Johannesburg: Central News Agency.
HENRICI, A. T. (1930). Molds, yeasts, and actinomycetes. New York: J. Wiley & Sons, Inc. (London: Chapman & Hall, Ltd.) [2nd Edit., see Skinner, C. E. et al., 1947.]
HENRICI, A. T. (1939). An endotoxin from Aspergillus fumigatus. J. Immunol. 36, 319-338.
HENRY, J. N. (1952). Mycotic dermatitis, or lumpy wool. N. S. W. Dep. Agric. Diseases of Animals leafl. No. 49, pp. 3.
HERMS, H. (1950). Über zwei Fälle von Morchelvergiftung beim Hunde. Berl. Münch. tierärztl. Wschr. No. 8. p. 161.
HEUSINGER, K. F. (1821). De metamorphosi rostri pici et de generatione mucoris in organismo animali vivente. Jena: typ. Schreiberei et soc.
HIDIROGLON, M. (1950). Treatment of epizootic lymphangitis with formol. Vet. Med. 45, 484 & 493.
HINDMARSH, W. L. & HART, L. (1937). Vet. Res. Rep. Dep. Agric. N. S. W. 1937. pp. 78-88.
HÖPPLI, R. (1923). Lungenveränderungen beim Kaninchen infolge Schimmelpilzinfektion. Z. InfektKr. Haustiere 24, 39-46.
HOERLEIN, A. B. (1945). Studies on animal dermatomycoses. I. Clinical studies. II. Cultural studies. Cornell Vet. 35, 287-298; 299-307.
HOLMES, J.D.E. (1908). A peculiar form of streptothricosis among cattle. J. trop. vet. Sci. 3, 289-300.
HOLZWORTH, J. (1952). Cryptococcosis in a cat. Cornell Vet. 42, 12-15.
HOLZWORTH, J. & COFFIN, D.L. (1953). Cryptococcosis in the cat: a second case. Cornell Vet. 43, 546-550.
HOOGLAND, H. J. M. (1932). Mucor-mycose bij een varken. Tijdschr. Diergeneesk. 59, 1156-1163.
HOPKIRK, C. S. M. (1936). Paspalum staggers. N. Z. J. Agric. 53, 105-108.
HORI, MICHINORI, YAMAMOTO, T., OZAWA, A., MATSUKI, Y., HAMAGUCHI, A. & SORAOKA, H. (1954). [Studies on a fungus species isolated from the malt-feed which caused mass death of cows. III. Classification of the isolated fungus, mechanism of its toxin production, and chemical nature of the toxin.] Jap. J. Bact. 9, 1105-1111. [In Japanese. English summary.]
HORNBY, H.E. (1920). A contagious impetigo of cattle. Vet. J. 76, 210-216.
HORTON-SMITH, C. & LONG, P. L. (1952). The effect of penotrane on the growth in vitro of Candida albicans and Aspergillus fumigatus. J. comp. Path. 62, 266-274.
HUDSON, C. B. (1947). Aspergillus fumigatus infection in the eyes of baby chicks. Poult. Sci. 26, 192-193.
HUDSON, J.R. (1937). Cutaneous streptothricosis. Proc. R. Soc. Med. 30, 1457-1460.
HÜLPHERS, G. & LILLEENGEN, K. (1947). Mögelsvampsinfektion, asper-

gillos, hos hare och vilt levande fågel. Svensk VetTidskr. 52, 235-239 & 243-262.

HULSE, E. C. (1952). An outbreak of mastitis in cattle caused by yeasts and the experimental reproduction of the condition. Vet. Rec. 64, 210-211.

HUMPHREYS, F. A. & HELMER, D. E. (1943). Pulmonary sporotrichosis in a cattle beast. Canad. J. comp. Med. 7, 199-204.

HUTCHINS. (1919). (Cited by Hornby, 1920.)

HUTYRA, F. & MAREK, J. (1922). Spezielle Pathologie und Therapie der Haustiere. 6th Edit. Vol. 3. p. 187. Jena: Gustav Fischer.

HYDE, H. A., RICHARDS, M. & WILLIAMS, D. A. (1956). Allergy to mould spores in Britain. Brit. med. J. 1, 886-890.

INNES, J. R. M., SEIBOLD, H.R. & ARENTZEN, W.P. (1952). The pathology of bovine mastitis caused by Cryptococcus neoformans. Amer. J. vet. Res. 13, 469-475.

IVANOV, X. (1949). Ustilagineous pneumonia in cattle. The spores of Ustilago maydis as a pathogenic factor. C. R Acad. bulg. Sci. 2, 49-52.

IVERSEN, L. & RØED, H (1950). Et tilfelle av abort hos storfe forårsaket av Aspergillus fumigatus. Nord. VetMed. 2, 992-996.

JAKL, J. (1949). Příspěvek k dermatomykosám u ovcí. [Dermatomycosis in sheep.] Sborn. čes. Akad. zemědělsk. Věd, Vet. Med. 22, 144-154.

JASPER, D. E. & LEWIS, J. S. (1951). Coccidioidomycosis in the dog. N. Amer. Vet. 32, 37-40.

JELLISON, W. L. (1950). Haplomycosis in Montana rabbits, rodents and carnivores. Publ. Hlth Rep., Wash. 65, 1057-1063.

JELLISON, W. L. (1954). The presence of a pulmonary fungus in Korean rodents. Publ. Hlth Rep., Wash. 69, 996-997.

JELLISON, W. L. (1956). Haplomycosis in Sweden. Nord. VetMed. 8, 504-506.

JILLSON, O.F. & BUCKLEY, W.R. (1951). Fungous disease in man acquired from cattle and horse (due to Trichophyton faviforme). New Engl. J. Med. 246, 996-999.

JONES, E. B. (1953). Ergot poisoning in young cattle. I. Vet. Rec. 65, 156-158.

JONES, T. C. & MAURER, F. C. (1944). Sporotrichosis in horses. Case report. Bull. U. S. Army med. Dep., Wash. No. 74, pp. 63-73.

JUNGHERR, E. (1935). Mycotic affections of the bovine reproductive system. J. Amer. vet. med. Ass. 86, 64-75.

JUNGHERR, E. L (1933). Observations on a severe outbreak of mycosis in chicks. J. agric. Res. 46, 169-178.

JUNGHERR, E. & GIFFORD, R. (1944). Three hitherto unreported turkey diseases in Connecticut. Erysipelas — hexamitiasis — mycotic encephalomalacia. Cornell Vet. 34, 214-226.

KANE, G. J., DOWNING, W. & WILSDON, A. J. (1955). Mycotic dermatitis in Great Britain. Vet. Rec. 67, 779.

KAPLAN, W. & GEORG, L.K. (1957). Isolation of Microsporum audouini from a dog. J. invest. Derm. 28, 313-315.

KAPLAN, W., GEORG, L. K. & FOSNAUGH, C. J. (1956). Isolation of the dermatophyte, Microsporum gypseum, from a horse with ringworm. J. Amer. vet. med. Ass. 129, 381-383.

KAPLAN, W., GEORG, L. K. & BROMLEY, C. L., Jr. (1957). Ringworm in cats caused by Microsporum gypseum. Vet. Med. 52, 347-349.

KAPLAN, W., GEORG, L. K., HENDRICKS, S. L. & LEEPER, R. A. (1957). Isolation of Microsporum distortum from animals in the United States. J. invest. Derm. 28, 449-453.

KAPLAN, W., HOPPING, J. L., Jr. & GEORG, L. K. (1957). Ringworm in horses caused by the dermatophyte Microsporum gypseum. J. Amer. vet. med. Ass. 131, 329-332.

KARPOVA-BENUA, E.I. (1954). [On toxic fungi in cotton fibres]. Bot. Zhur. SSSR. 39, 488-497.

KAUFMANN, M. (1908). Rapport sur les résultats obtenus par la commission d'études pour la détermination de la dose d'ergot à tolérer dans l'avoine algérienne. Rec. Méd. vét. 85, 293-299.

KAUKER, E. (1955). Über Mastitis-Blastomyceten. Berl. Münch. tierärztl. Wschr. 68, 407-409.

KEMENES, F. (1954). Über einen Fall von Coccidioidomykose bei einem Kaninchen in Ungarn. Acta microbiol., Acad. Sci. Hung. 2, 191-194.

KENNEDY, W. K. & SCHENK, R. U. (1954). The use of fungicides in the preservation of moist hay. Agron. J. 46, 252-257.

KIKUCHI, K. (1923). Über einen Fall von Blastomykose beim Pferd. J. Jap. Soc. vet. Sci. 2, 415.

KIMBALL, A. & FRANK, E. R. (1945). The isolation of Actinomyces bovis from fistulous withers and poll evil. Amer. J. vet. Res. 6, 39-44.

KIMBALL, A., TWIEHAUS, M. J. & FRANK, E.R. (1954). Actinomyces bovis isolated from six cases of bovine orchitis. A preliminary report. Amer. J. vet. Res. 15, 551-553.

KING, N. B. (1946). 'Favus' or white comb disease of poultry. Agric. Gaz. N. S. W. 57, 499-500.

KINGMAN, H. E. & PALEN, J. S. (1951). Streptomycin in the treatment of actinomycosis. J. Amer. vet. med. Ass. 118, 28-30.

KIRK, H. (1946). Organo-mercury compounds in veterinary medicine. Vet. Rec. 58, 299-300.

KOEN, J. S. & SMITH, H. C. (1945). An unusual case of genital involvement in swine associated with eating moldy corn. Vet. Med. 40, 131-133.

KOMURO, S., AOKI, Y. & ODASHIMA, S. (1952). On microsporon sapporense. Sapporo med. J. 3, 1-13.

KOTLIAR, E. (1894). Contribution à l'étude de la pseudo-tuberculose aspergillaire. Ann. Inst. Pasteur 8, 479-489.

KOVALEV, A. A. (1947). [Mycotic aphthous stomatitis in suckling pigs.] Veterinariya, Moscow 24, No. 1. p. 18.

KRAL, F. (1953a). Skin diseases of large animals. Vet. Med. 48, 173-177.

KRAL, F. (1953b). Skin diseases of small animals. Vet. Med. 48, 185-192.

KRAL, F. (1955). Classification, symptomatology, and recent treatment of animal dermatomycoses (ringworm). J. Amer. vet. med. Ass. 127, 395-402.

KREMBS, J. (1937). Seltene Schimmelpilzerkrankung bei einem Rehkiss. Dtsch. Jägerztg. No. 44.

KRISHNAMURTI AYYAR, V. (1927). Studies in Bovine Lymphangitis. Mem. Dep. Agric. India, Vet. 4, 103-127. (8 Pl.)

LAHAYE, J. (1928). Maladies des pigeons et des poules, des oiseaux de basse-cour et de volière. pp. 393. Remonchamps: Steinmetz-Haenen.

LALL, H. K. & RAJAGOPALAN, V. R. (1949). Actinomycotic dermatitis in cross Merino lambs. Indian J. vet. Sci. 19, 1-4.

LANGHAM, R. F. (1955). Coccidioidomycosis in a dog. J. Amer. vet. med. Ass. 127, 336-337.

LAPČEVIĆ, E., PRIBIĆEVIĆ, S. & KOZIĆ, L. (1953). Trovanje konja prouzrokovačem crne rde – Puccinia graminis. Vet. Glasn. 7, 268-271.

LARSH, H. W., HINTON, A. & COZAD. G. C. (1956). Natural reservoir of Histoplasma capsulatum. Amer. J. Hyg. 63, 18-27.

La TOUCHE, C. J. (1952a). The Leeds campaign against microsporosis in children and domestic animals. Vet. Rec. 64, 398-399.

La TOUCHE, C. J. (1952b). Some observations on ringworm in calves due to Trichophyton discoides Sabouraud. Vet. Rec. 64, 841-843.

La TOUCHE, C. J. (1953). Some clinical and microscopic features of Microsporum canis Bodin infection of the skin and its appendages as it occurs in the cat. Vet. Rec. 65, 680-681.

La TOUCHE, C. J. (1955). Onychomycosis in cats infected by Microsporum canis Bodin. Vet. Rec. 67, 578-579.

LEBASQUE, J. (1933). Les champignons des teignes du cheval et des bovidés. Thesis, Paris.

LEBASQUE, J. (1934). Recherches morphologiques et biologiques sur les Trichophyton mégasporés du cheval et du boeuf. Ann. Parasit. hum. comp. 12, 418-444.

LEBER, T. (1882). Ueber die Wachsthumsbedingungen der Schimmelpilze im menschlichen und thierischen Körper. Berl. klin. Wschr. 19, 161-164 & 301.

LEEMANN, A. C. (1933). A short summary on our botanical knowledge of Lolium temulentum L. Onderstepoort J. vet. Sci. 1, 213-218.

LERCHE, M. (1952). Eine durch Algen (Prototheca) hervorgerufene Mastitis der Kuh. Berl. Münch. tierärztl. Wschr. 65, 64-69.

LERNAU C., SHAPIRO, A. & ASCHNER M. (1947). Yeast infection of the udder after irrigation with penicillin. Refuah vet. 4, 36-37.

LESBOUYRIES, G. (1941). La pathologie des oiseaux. pp. 868. Paris: Vigot Frères. 2 Vols.

LESBOUYRIES, G. (1952). Actinophytose à Streptothrix actinomyces chez le mouton. Rec. Méd. vét. 128, 465-476.

LEVINE, N. D., DUNLAP, G. L. & GRAHAM, R. (1938). An intracellular parasite encountered in ferret. Cornell Vet. 28, 249-251.

LEVITSKII, B. G. & KONYUKHOVA, V. A. (1947). [On the toxicity of feed contaminated with common fungi.] Veterinariya, Moscow 24, No. 10. pp. 40-43.

LEWIS, E. F. (1947). Penicillin therapy in actinomycosis in cattle. Vet. Rec. 59, 435.

LICHTHEIM, L. (1882). Ueber pathogene Schimmelpilze. I. Die Aspergillusmykosen. Berl. klin. Wschr. 19, 129-132 & 147-152.

LICHTHEIM, L. (1884). Ueber pathogene Schimmelpilze. II. Ueber pathogene Mucorineen und die durch sie erzeugten Mykosen des Kaninchens. Z. klin. Med. 7, 140-177.

LIGNIÈRES & PETIT. (1898). Péritonite aspergillaire des dindon. Rec. Méd. vét. 75, 145-149.

LINDT, W. (1886). Mitteilungen über einige neue pathogene Schimmelpilze. Arch. exp. Path. Pharmak. 21, 269-298.

LITTMAN, M. L. & ZIMMERMAN, L. E. (1956). Cryptococcosis. pp. 205. New York: Grune & Stratton.

LODDER, J. & VAN RIJ, J. W. Kreger (1952). The yeasts: a taxonomic study. Amsterdam: North Holland Publishing Co.

LOGINOV, V. P. (1958). [Acute fusariotoxicosis in piglets.] Veterinariya,

Moscow 35, No. 1. pp. 67-68.
LOMAS, H. (1939). Ringworm in horses – incidence and control. Vet. J. 95, 290-292.
LONG, H. C. (1924). Plants poisonous to live stock. 2nd Edit. pp. 120. Cambridge University Press.
LOONEY, J.M. & STEIN, T. (1950). Coccidioidomycosis. The hazard involved in diagnostic procedures, with report of a case. New Engl. J. Med. 242, 77-82.
LOOSLI, C. G., GRAYSTON, J. T., ALEXANDER, E. R. & TANZI, F. (1952). Epidemiological studies of pulmonary histoplasmosis in a farm family. Amer. J. Hyg. 55, 392-401.
LUBARSKY, R. & PLUNKETT, O. A. (1955). In vitro production of the spherule phase of Coccidioides immitis. J. Bact. 70, 182-186.
LUCET, A. (1897). De l'Aspergillus fumigatus chez animaux domestiques et dans les oeufs en incubation. Étude clinique et expérimentale. 108 pp. Paris: Ch. Mendel.
LURIE, H. I. (1948). A common antigenic factor in different species of Sporotrichum. Mycologia 40, 106-113.
LURIE, H. I. (1950). Pathogenic Sporotricha; their carbohydrate reactions. Mycologia 42, 624-641.
LURIE, H. I. (1951). Sporotrichum species: their nitrogen metabolism. Mycologia 43, 117-129.
MACAIGNE, M. & NICAUD, P. (1927a). Recherches sur la sporo-agglutination dans l'aspergillose pulmonaire. C. R. Soc. Biol. Paris 96, 444-445.
MACAIGNE, M. & NICAUD, P. (1927b). Recherches sur les réactions antigéniques dans l'aspergillose. Intra dermo reáction antigénique focale. C. R. Soc. Biol. Paris 96, 446-448.
McDIARMID, A., & AUSTWICK, P. K. C. (1954). Occurrence of Haplosporangium parvum in the lungs of the mole (Talpa europaea). Nature, Lond. 174, 843-844.
McERLEAN, B. A. (1952). Vulvovaginitis of swine. Vet. Rec. 64, 539-540.
McGAUGHEY, C. A. & BANDARANAYAKE, A. (1953). Moniliasis in guinea-fowl chicks and other poultry. Ceylon vet. J. 1, 43-44.
McGRATH, J. T. (1954). Cryptococcosis of the central nervous system in domestic animals. Amer. J. Path. 30, 651.
McKENNEY, F. D., TRAUM, J. & BONESTELL, A.E. (1944). Acute coccidiomycosis in a mountain gorilla (Gorilla beringeri) with anatomical notes. J. Amer. vet. med. Ass. 104, 136-140.
MACKINNON, J. (1956). Ann. Rep. Dir. Vet. Services Federation of Rhodesia and Nyasaland. p. 97.
MACKINNON, J. E. (1936). Epizootia de tiña en caballos y contaminación del hombre. Arch. urug. Med. 8, 498-502.
MACKINNON, J.E. (1949a). The dependence on the weather of the incidency of sporotrichosis. Mycopathologia 4, 367-374.
MACKINNON, J. E. (1949b). Estadística sobre 1000 casos de micosis cutáneas en el Uruguay y determinacion de las especies causantes. An. Inst. Hig. Montevideo 3, 83-94.
MACKINNON, J. E. & ARTAGAVEYTIA-ALLENDE, R. C. (1948). Vitamin deficiencies of seven strains of ectothrix, large spored trichophytons isolated from man and cattle. J. Bact. 56, 91-96.
McNUTT, S. H., PURWIN, P. & MURRAY, C. (1928). Vulvovaginitis in swine. Preliminary report. J. Amer. vet. med. Ass. 73, 484-492.

McPHERSON, E. A. (1956). Trichophyton mentagrophytes: natural infection in pigs. Vet. Rec. 68, 710-711.

McPHERSON, E.A. (1957a). A survey of the incidence of ringworm in cattle in Northern Britain. Vet. Rec. 69, 674-679.

McPHERSON, E. A. (1957b). The influence of physical factors on dermatomycosis in domestic animals. Vet. Rec. 69, 1010-1013.

MADDY, K. T. (1954a). Coccidioidomycosis of cattle in the southwestern United States. J. Amer. vet. med. Ass. 124, 456-464.

MADDY, K. T. (1954b). Coccidioidomycosis in a sheep. J. Amer. vet. med. Ass. 124, 465.

MADSEN, D. E. (1942). Some studies of three pathogenic fungi isolated from animals. Cornell Vet. 32, 383-389.

de MAGALHAES, O. (1935). Ensaios de Mycologia. Mem. Inst. Osw. Cruz 30, 1-55.

MAGNUSSON, H. (1928). The commonest forms of actinomycosis in domestic animals and their etiology. Acta path. microbiol. scand. 5, 170-245.

MANDLIK, G. S. (1937). A record of rhinosporidial polypi, with some observations on the mode of infection. Indian med. Gaz. 72, 143-147.

MANGRULKAR, M. Y. (1938). "Actinomycosis" and actinobacillosis in animals in India. Indian J. vet. Sci. 8, 271-291.

MATSUMOTO, T. (1929). Investigation of aspergilli by serological methods. Trans. Brit. mycol. Soc. 14, 69-88.

MATTHÉAKIS, E. (1953). [Sporotrichosis in a mule.] Delt. Hellen. kten. Hetair. 2, 428-436. [In Greek. French summary.]

MATTHIAS, D. (1941). Soor des Pansens bei einem Kalbe. Tierärztl. Rdsch. 47, 477-478.

MAUNDER, J.C.J. (1936). Ergotism in dairy cattle. Qd agric. J. 45, 250-251.

MAYER, A. C. & EMMERT. (1815). Verschimmelung (Mucedo) im lebenden Körper. Dtsch. Arch. Anat. Physiol. (Meckl.) 1, 310, (Cited by Urbain & Guillot, 1938.)

MAYO, N. S. (1891). Bull. Kansas agric. Exp. Sta. No. 24.

MAZZANTI(?NI). (1884). Jber. K. Centr. Thier. München (Cited by Bournay, 1895.)

de MELLO, M.T. (1946). Estudos sobre o Rhinosporidium seeberi. Thesis, Rio de Janeiro pp. 131-239.

de MELLO, M. T. (1949). Rhinosporidiosis. Mycopathologia 4, 342-348.

MENGES, R. W. (1951a). Canine histoplasmosis. J. Amer. vet. med. Ass. 119, 411-415.

MENGES, R. W. (1951b). The histoplasmin skin test in animals. J. Amer. vet. med. Ass. 119, 69-71.

MENGES, R. W. (1954). Histoplasmin sensitivity in animals. Cornell Vet. 44, 21-31.

MENGES, R. W., FURCOLOW, M. L. & HABERMANN, R. T. (1954). An outbreak of histoplasmosis involving animals and man. Amer. J. vet. Res. 15, 520-524.

MENGES, R. W., FURCOLOW, M. L. & RUHE, J. S. (1950). Experimental histoplasmosis in a dog. A non-fatal case. Publ. Hlth Rep., Wash. 65, 628-631.

MENGES, R. W. & GEORG, L. K. (1955). Animal ringworm study. Vet. Med. 50, 293-297.

MENGES, R. W. & GEORG, L. K. (1956). An epizootic of ringworm among guinea pigs caused by Trichophyton mentagrophytes. J. Amer. vet. med. Ass. 128, 395-398.

MENGES, R. W. & GEORG, L. K. (1957a). Survey of animal ringworm in the United States. Publ. Hlth Rep., Wash. 72, 503-509.
MENGES, R.W. & GEORG, L.K. (1957b). Canine ringworm caused by Microsporum gypseum. Cornell Vet. 47, 90-100.
MENGES, R.W., GEORG, L.K. & HABERMANN, T. (1957). Therapeutic studies on ringworm-infected guinea pigs. J. invest. Derm. 28, 233-237.
MENGES, R. W. & HABERMANN, R. T. (1954). Isolation of Haplosporangium parvum from soil and results of experimental inoculations. Amer. J. Hyg. 60, 106-116.
MENGES, R. W. & KINTNER, L. D. (1951). Bovine histoplasmosis. Case report. N. Amer. Vet. 32, 692-695.
MENGES, R.W., LARSH, H.W. & HABERMANN, R.T. (1953). Canine actinomycosis. A report of two cases. J. Amer. vet. med. Ass. 122, 73-78.
di MENNA, M. E. (1955a). A search for pathogenic species of yeasts in New Zealand soils. J. gen. Microbiol. 12, 54-62.
di MENNA, M. E. (1955b). A quantitative study of air-borne fungus spores in Dunedin, New Zealand. Trans. Brit. mycol. Soc. 38, 119-129.
MENZIES, D. W. (1958). Unpublished report. [Copies available from Commonwealth Bureau of Animal Health, Weybridge, Surrey.]
MEYER, E. & VERGES, P. (1950). Mouse pathogenicity as a diagnostic aid in the identification of Actinomyces bovis. J. Lab. clin. Med. 36, 667-674.
MEYER, K.F. (1913). Blastomycosis in dogs. Proc. path. Soc. Philad. 15, 10.
MEYER, K. F. (1914). A pathogenic Blastomyces from the horse. Proc. path. Soc. Philad. 16, 28.
MITCHELL, D. T. (1918a). A condition produced in cattle feeding on maize infected with Diplodia zeae. 7th & 8th Repts. Dir. Vet. Res. April 1918, pp. 425-437.
MITCHELL, D. T. (1918b). The effects of C. paspali on cattle. 7th & 8th Repts. Dir. Vet. Res. S. Africa. April 1918, pp. 440-449.
MITCHELL, H. H. & BEADLES, J. R. (1940). The impairment in nutritive value of corn grain damaged by specific fungi. J. agric. Res. 61, 135-141.
MOHLER, J. R. & SHAHAN, M. S. (1943). Lumpy jaw, or actinomycosis. Circ. U. S. Dep. Agric. No. 438, pp. 9. [Revised.]
MOMBERG-JÖRGENSEN, H. C. (1950). Enzoötic mycosis in mink. Amer. J. vet. Res. 11, 334-338.
de MONBREUN, W. A. & ANDERSON, K. (1939). The dog as a natural host for Histoplasma capsulatum. Report of a case of histoplasmosis in this animal. Amer. J. trop. Med. 19, 565-587.
MOORE, E. N. (1953). Aspergillus fumigatus as a cause of ophthalmitis in turkeys. Poult. Sci. 32, 796-799.
MOORE, M., RUSSELL, W. O. & SACHS, E. (1946). Chronic leptomeningitis and ependymitis caused by Ustilago, probably U. zeae (corn smut). Ustilagomycosis, the second reported instance of human infection. Amer. J. Path. 22, 761-777.
MOORE, W.C., SMITH, A. & PETHYBRIDGE, G.H. (1934). Report on fungus, bacterial and other diseases of crops in England & Wales. 1928-1932. Bull. Minist. Agric., Lond. No. 79. pp. 117.
MOREIRA-JACOB, M. & van UDEN, N. (1956). Mycotic abortion in cattle. A case record and a review of the relevant literature. Brit. vet. J. 112, 453-461.
MORI, N. (1916). Natura ifomicetica dei corpuscoli della pleuropneumonite

essudativa della capre. Il germe specifico è un aspergillo. Pathologica 8, 311-315.

MORNET, P. & THIÉRY, G. (1955). Streptothricose cutanée des bovins. Bull. epiz. Dis. Afr. 3, 302-324.

MORQUER, R. & COMBY, L. (1942). Etude biologique d'un Actinomyces nouveau, pathogène pour le cheval. C. R. Soc. Biol. Paris 136, 703.

MORQUER, R., PUGET, E. & BAZEX, A. (1953). Sur un nouvel agent de blastomycose chez le chien. C. R. Acad. Sci., Paris 236, 546-548.

MORQUER, R., PUGET, E. & BAZEX, A. (1954a). Une nouvelle levure pathogène, Candida pseudotumoralis. Étude systématique et physiologique. Rev. Mycol. 19, 63-84.

MORQUER, R., PUGET, E. & BAZEX, A. (1954b). Blastomycose du chien (Candida pseudotumoralis). Anatomie et étiologie. Rev. Méd. vét 105, 783-801.

MUENDE, I. & WEBB, P. (1937). Ringworm fungus growing as a saprophyte under natural conditions. Arch. Derm. Syph., Chicago 36, 987-990.

MUNCH-PETERSEN, E. (1954). Actinomyces (Nocardia) sp. from a bovine udder infection. Aust. vet. J. 30, 297-300.

MURPHY, J. M. & DRAKE, C. H. (1947). Infection of the bovine udder with yeastlike fungi. Amer. J. vet. Res. 8, 43-51.

NAUMOV, N. A. (1939). Clés des Mucorinées (Mucorales). Vol. 9 of Encyclopédie mycologique. Paris: Paul Lechevalier.

NEEFS & GILLAIN. (1931). Contribution à l'étude de la teigne. Ann. Méd. vét. 76, 193-209.

NEGRONI, P. (1932). Trichophyton lacticolor de la teigne spontanée du cobaye. C. R. Soc. Biol., Paris 110, 140-141.

NEILL, J. C. (1941). The endophytes of Lolium and Festuca. N. Z. J. Sci. Tech. Sect. A. 23, 185-193.

NEILL, J. C. (1952). Note on agronomic effect of the endophyte of Lolium perenne. N. Z. J. Sci. Tech. Sect. A. 34, 230.

NEILL, J.M., SUGG, J.Y. & McCAULEY, D. W. (1951). Serologically reactive material in spinal fluid, blood, and urine from a human case of cryptococcosis (torulosis). Proc. Soc. exp. Biol., N. Y. 77, 775-778.

NEUMANN, L. G. (1909). Parasites et maladies parasitaires des oiseaux domestiques. pp. 230. Paris: Asselin et Houzeau.

NEWBERNE, J. W., NEAL, J. E. & HEATH, M. K. (1955). Some clinical and microbiological observations on four cases of canine blastomycosis. J. Amer. vet. med. Ass. 127, 220-223.

NEWSOM, I.E., STOUT, E.N., THORP, F., Jr., BARBER, C.W. & GROTH, A.H. (1937). Oat hay poisoning. J. Amer. vet. med. Ass. 90, 66-75.

NICAUD, P. (1928). Les lésions expérimentales dans l'aspergillose. Les formes actinomycosiques de l'Aspergillus fumigatus. C. R. Soc. Biol. Paris 99, 1564-1565 & 1565-1567.

NICKERSON, W. J. & MANKOWSKI, Z. (1953). A polysaccharide medium of known composition favoring chlamydospore formation in Candida albicans. J. infect. Dis. 92, 20-25.

NICOLAUS, W. (1934). Ueber Histogenese und Altersbestimmung der durch Aspergillus fumigatus hervorgerufenen Veränderungen bei Hühnern. Z. InfektKr. Haustiere 45, 191-209.

NIELSEN, M. (1902-03). Skimmelvegetation i Kindhulen hos en Hest. Maanedsskr. Dyrlaeg. 14, 622-624.

NIELSEN, N. (1929). Mucormykose beim Schwein. II. Mitteilung: Beschreibung der isolierten Pilze. Virchows Arch. 273, 859-863.

NISBET, D.I. & BANNATYNE, C.C. (1955). A dermatitis of sheep associated with an organism of the genus Actinomyces. Vet. Rec. 67, 713-715.
NOBEL, T. A. & SHAMIR, A. (1956). [Congenital mycosis in a lamb.] [In Hebrew.] Refuah vet. 13, 23-24. English summary p. 37.
NOCARD, M. E. (1888). Note sur la maladie des boeufs de la Guadeloupe. Ann. Inst. Pasteur 2, 293-302.
NÖLLER, W. & KRAUSE, C. (1924). Ein Beitrag zu den Pneumonomykosen des Pferdes. Z. InfektKr. Haustiere 25, 81-108.
NORDÉN, Å. (1951). Sporotrichosis. Clinical and laboratory features and a serologic study in experimental animals and humans. Acta path. microbiol. scand., Suppl. 89, pp. 119.
NORDSKOG, A. W. (1946). Reproductive failure and agalactia in ergotized female rats. Amer. J. vet. Res. 7, 490-497.
NORDSKOG, A. W. & CLARK, R. T. (1945). Ergotism in pregnant sows, female rats and guinea pigs. Amer. J. vet. Res. 6, 107-116.
NUVOLETTI & CASELLA. (1903). (Cited by Wyssmann, 1941.)
OBICI, A. (1898). Ueber die pathogenen Eigenschaften des Aspergillus fumigatus. Beitr. path. Anat. 23, 197-237.
OEHL. (1929). Lymphangitis epizootica beim Schwein. Ein Beitrag zur Kasuistik. Dtsch. tierärztl. Wschr. 37, 39-40.
OLSON, J. R. (1947). Sporotrichosis in a mule. Vet. Stud., (Iowa) 9, 165-167.
OSBORNE, A.D. (1949). Unpublished report. [Copies available from Commonwealth Bureau of Animal Health, Weybridge, Surrey.]
OTA, M. & GAILLARD, H. (1926). Sur une teigne trichophytique d'un bovidé du Cameroun produite par une espèce nouvelle de Grubyella, G. camerounensis n. sp. Ann. Parasit. hum. comp. 4, 14-21.
OTTE, W. (1928). Die Krankheiten des Geflügels mit besonderer Berücksichtigung der Anatomie und der Hygiene. pp. 214. Berlin: Rich. Schoetz Verlag.
OWEN, R. (1832). On the anatomy of the flamingo (Phœnicopterus ruber, Linn.). Proc. zool. Soc. Lond. 2, 141-144.
OXER, D. T. (1930). Mycotic dermatitis in sheep; and green staining of wool. Tasm. J. Agric. 1, 120-121.
PALLASKE, G. (1939). Mukormykose beim Schwein. Tierärztl. Rdsch. 45, 601-603.
PALLASKE. (1944). Die Hautkrankheiten des Pferdes und ihre Bekämpfung. Mitt. Landw., Berl. 59, 338-340. [Abst. in Rev. med. vet. Mycol. 1, 834 (1946).]
PALLASKE, G. (1952). Beitrag zur Streptotrichose des Hundes. Berl. Münch. tierärztl. Wschr. 65, 190-194.
PALLIN, W. A. (1904). A treatise on Epizootic lymphangitis. 2nd Edit. pp. 57 + xxiii (& index). London: University Press of Liverpool.
PALMEIRO, J. M. (1946). Noticia do resultado do emprego de um tipo de vacina contra a linfangite epizoótica. Rev. med. vet., Lisboa 41, 436-438.
PALTAUF, A. (1885). Mycosis mucorina. Eine Beitrag zur Kenntniss der Menschlichen Fadenpilzerkrankungen. Virchows Arch. 102, 543-564.
PAMMEL, L. H. (1911). A manual of poisonous plants. The Torch Press, Chedar Rapids, Iowa. (Cited by Steyn, 1933.)
PARÁ, M. (1946). Histoplasmosis in Brazil. Amer. J. trop. Med. 26, 273-292.
PARISH, H. J. & CRADDOCK, S. (1931). A ringworm epizootic in mice.

Brit. J. exp. Path 12, 209-212.
PARLIER. (1936). Le bi-iodure de mercure dans le traitement de la lymphangite épizootique. Rev. vét. milit. 20, 387-401.
PARNES, J. (1938). Beitrag zur Chemotherapie der Lymphangitis epiz. equ. Berl. Münch. tierärztl. Wschr. 10 June, 335-337.
PATERSON, J. D. (1954). Personal communication.
PAYNTER, H.S. (1954). Deep mycoses in Hawaii; histoplasmin, coccidioidin, haplosporangin and blastomycin sensitivity and a review of cases of mycoses. Hawaii med. J. 13, 189-194.
PEARSON, L. & RAVENEL, M. P. (1900). A case of pneumonomycosis due to Aspergillus fumigatus. J. comp. Med. 21, 451-465.
PELOURO, J. T. (1943). Um caso de actinomicose ocular em bovino. Repos. Lab. Pat. vet., Lisboa 5, 235-239.
PEPPLER, H.J. & TWIEHAUS, M.J. (1942). Equine sporotrichosis. Trans. Kans. Acad. Sci. 45, 40-46.
PIER, A. C., GRAY, D. M. & FOSSATTI, M. J. (1958). Nocardia asteroides — a newly recognised pathogen of the mastitis complex. J. Amer. vet. med. Ass. 132, 170-171.
PIERCY, P. L., HARGIS, G. & BROWN, C. A. (1944). Mushroom poisoning in cattle. J. Amer. vet. med. Ass. 105, 206-208.
PILLAI, P. B. K. (1953). Canine nocardiosis; abdominal form; treatment with penicillin and streptomycin. Ceylon vet. J. 1, 32-33.
PIRATININGA, S. N. (1943). Esporotricose em muar. Rev. Fac. Med. vet., S. Paulo 2, 219-222.
PLAZIKOWSKI, U. (1935). Soor-sjuka hos höns. Skand. VetTidskr. 25, 682-697.
PLOWRIGHT, W. (1956). Cutaneous streptothricosis of cattle: I. Introduction and epizootiological features in Nigeria. Vet. Rec. 68, 350-355.
PLUM, N. (1932). Verschiedene Hyphomyceten-Arten als Ursache sporadischer Fälle von Abortus beim Rinde. Acta. path. microbiol. scand. 9, 150-157.
PLUNKETT, J. J. (1949). Epizootic lymphangitis. J. R. Army vet. Cps. 20, 94-99.
PORGES, N., MULLER, J. F. & LOCKWOOD, L. B. (1935). A mucor found in fowl. Mycologia 27, 330-331.
PORTER, I. A. (1953). Actinomycosis in Scotland. Brit. med. J. Nov. 14th, 1084-1086.
POUNDEN, W. D., AMBERSON, J. M. & JAEGER, R. F. (1952). A severe mastitis problem associated with Cryptococcus neoformans in a large dairy herd. Amer. J. vet. Res. 13, 121-128.
PRCHAL, C. J. (1948). Coccidioidomycosis of cattle in Arizona. J. Amer. vet. med. Ass. 112, 461-465.
PREININGER, T. (1937). Durch Maisbrand (Ustilago maydis) bedingte Dermatomykose. Arch. Derm. Syph., Wien. 176, 109-113.
PRÉVOT, A. R. (1953). Morphologie, physiologie, pouvoir pathogène et systématique des Actinomycétales anaérobies. In Symposium on Actinomycetales. Suppl. to Proc. 6th Internat. Microbiol. Congr. Rome 1953. pp. 40-68. [Rome: Fondazione Emanuele Paterno.]
PRIETO, D. & PIRES, A. (1944). A propósito de la rhinosporidiosis. Presentación de un caso en un caballo. Gac. vet., B. Aires 6, 323-336.
PULLAR, E. M. (1939). The treatment of actinomycosis by the intravenous administration of sodium iodide. Aust. vet. J. 15, 104-117.
PULLAR, E. M. & LEREW, W. M. (1937). Vulvovaginitis of swine. Aust. vet.

J. 13, 28-31.
QUIN, A.H. (1952). Newer problems in swine diseases — control and treatment. Canad. J. comp. Med. 16, 265-270.
QUINLAN, J. & de KOCK, G. (1926). Two cases of rhinosporidiosis in equines. S. Afr. J. Sci. 23, 589-594.
RAINES, T. V., KUZDAS, C. D., WINKEL, F. H. & JOHNSON, B. S. (1956). Encephalitic aspergillosis in turkeys — a case report. J. Amer. vet. med. Ass. 129, 435-436.
RAJAGOPALAN, V. R. (1945). Lumpy wool or mycotic dermatitis in lambs. Indian Fmg 6, 222.
RAMSBOTTOM, J. (1953). Mushrooms and toadstools. New Naturalist, Collins, London. pp. 306.
RAMSEY, F. K. & CARTER, G. R. (1952). Canine blastomycosis in the United States. J. Amer. vet. med. Ass. 120, 93-98.
RANDALL, C. C., ORR, M. F. & SCHELL, F. G. (1951). Detection by tissue culture of an organism resembling Histoplasma capsulatum in an apparently healthy horse. Proc. Soc. exp. Biol., N. Y. 78, 447-450.
RANNAUD. (1950). Mycoses chez les équidés d'Indochine. "Sporotrichose". Rev. vét. milit. No. 2, 183-189.
RAO, M. Anant Narayan (1938). Rhinosporidiosis in bovines in the Madras Presidency, with a discussion on the probable modes of infection. Indian J. vet. Sci. 8, 187-198.
RAYER & MONTAGNE. (1842). Mycose aspergillaire dans les poches aériennes d'un bouvreuil. Journal l'Institut Paris p. 270. Muller's Archiv. 1842 p. 270. (Cited by Urbain & Guillot, 1938).
RAYMOND, F. (1910). Infectious lymphangitis in cattle. J. trop. vet. Sci. 5, 213-232.
RECTOR, L.E. & RECTOR, E.J. (1948). Coccidioidomycosis in the salivary gland of the Townsend mole. Amer. J. trop. med. 28, 707-709.
REDAELLI, G. (1957a). Ricerche sulle mastiti micotiche. I. Riproduzione sperimentale della mastite criptococcica. Arch. Vet. Ital. 8, 39-65.
REDAELLI, G. (1957b). Ricerche sulle mastiti micotiche. II. Controllo sperimentale dell'azione patogena di alcuni blastomiceti sporigeni ed asporigeni (Saccharomyces, Hansenula, Pichia, Torulopsis e Candida) per la mammella degli animali da latte. Arch. Vet. Ital. 8, 97-120.
REICH, W. J. & NECHTOW, M. J. (1949). Canine genital moniliasis as a source of reinfection in the human female. J. Amer. med. Ass. 141, 991-992.
REID, H. A. (1921). Notes on certain cases of dermatomycosis of cattle. Vet. J. 77, 21-23.
RÉNON, L. (1897). Etude sur l'aspergillose chez les animaux et chez l'homme. Paris: Masson et cie. pp. 301.
REWELL, R. E. & AINSWORTH, G. C. (1947). Occurrence of Aspergillus fumigatus Fresen. in the lung of an American bison. Nature, Lond. 160, 362-363.
RICHMAN, H. (1948). Histoplasmosis in a colt. N. Amer. Vet. 29, 710.
RIES, J.-N. (1903). Gutturomycose chez le cheval. Rec. Méd. vét. 10, 225-229.
RIVOLTA. (1856). ?7. Med. vet., Modena. (Cited by Bournay, 1895.)
RIVOLTA. (1885). G. Anat-physiol. Patol. Anim. Cited by Christiansen, 1929.)
ROBBINS, E.S. (1954). North American blastomycosis in the dog. J. Amer. vet. med. Ass. 125, 391-398.

ROBINSON, V. B. (1951). Nasal granuloma – a report of two cases in cattle. Amer. J. vet. Res. 12, 85-89.
ROBINSON, V. B. & SCHELL, F. G. (1951). Blastomycosis in a dog. Case report. N. Amer. Vet. 32, 555-558.
RODERICK, L. M., KIMBALL, A., McLEOD, W. M. & FRANK, E. R. (1948). A study of equine fistulous withers and poll evil. A complex infection with Actinomyces bovis and Brucella. Amer. J. vet. Res. 9, 5-10.
RODERICK, L.M. & SCHALK, A F. (1931). Studies on Sweet Clover Disease. Tech. Bull. Agric. exp. Sta. N. Dakota Agric. Coll. No. 250. pp. 56. (July 1931).
ROLLE, M. (1934). Hefe als Ursache für Euterentzündungen bei Kühen. Dtsch. tierärztl. Wschr. 42, 385-386.
ROLLE, M. & KOLB, E. (1954). Zur Frage des Vorkommens von Schimmelpilzen (Mucoraceae, Aspergillaceae) im Magen-Darmkanal der Haustiere. Z. Hyg. InfektKr. 139, 415-420.
ROLLINSON, D. H. L. & HAQ, I. (1948). Mycotic infection of the prepuce of the bull. Vet. Rec. 60, 69-70.
ROMANOV, N. A. (1928). Eine durch Meningitis komplizierte Schimmelpilzerkrankung der Stirnhöhle bei einem Pferde. Arch. wiss. prakt. Tierheilk. 58, 634-643.
ROUSSEAU, E. & SERRURIER. (1841). Développement de cryptogames sur les tissues de vertébrés vivants. C. R. Acad. Sci., Paris 13, 18-19.
ROWLEY, D.A., HABERMAN, R.T. & EMMONS, C.W. (1954). Histoplasmosis: pathological studies of fifty cats and fifty dogs from Loudoun County, Virginia. J. infect. Dis. 95, 98-108.
ROWSELL, H. C. (1955). In Report of the Ontario Veterinary College, 1954 pp. 16 & 17.
ROZHDESTVENSKII, N.A. (1927). [Ergot. A summary of present knowledge of ergot.] Materialui po mikologii i fitopatologii. 6, No. 1. pp. 123-165. [In Russian.] (Cited by Sarkisov, 1954, p. 33.)
RUHE, J. S. & CAZIER, P. D. (1949). A review of histoplasmosis. J. Amer. vet. med. Ass. 115, 47-50.
RYFF, J. F. (1953). Encephalitis in a deer due to Actinomyces bovis. J. Amer. vet. med. Ass. 122, 78-80.
SABOURAUD, R., SUIS, A. & SUFFRAN, F. (1909). La 'crête blanche' (favus) de la poule et son parasite. Rev. vét., Toulouse 34, 601-613 & 672-688.
Van SACEGHEM, R. (1915). Dermatose contagieuse (Impétigo contagieux). Bull. Soc. Pat. exot. 8, 354-359.
Van SACEGHEM, R. (1916). Étude complémentaire sur la dermatose contagieuse (Impétigo contagieux). Bull. Soc. Pat. exot. 9, 290-293.
Van SACEGHEM, R. (1934). La Dermatose, dite contagieuse des Bovidés. Impétigo Tropical des Bovidés. Bull. agric. Congo belge 25, 590-598.
SAHAI, L. (1938). Rhinosporidiosis in equines. Indian J. vet. Sci. 8, 221-223.
SALGUES, R. (1937). Les propriétés fongicides préventives du bleu de méthylène en pathologie animale. C.R. Acad. Sci., Paris 204, 721-723.
SALISBURY, R. M. (1949). Poultry diseases caused by mould and yeast infections. N. Z. J. Agric. 79, 558.
SALLES GOMES, C.E., FREITAS, D.C. & CUNHA, J.M.V. (1954). Tricofícia em bovinos por Trichophyton megnini Blanchard, 1895 (T. rosaceum Sabouraud 1909). Rev. Fac. Med. vet., S. Paulo 5, 177-182.
SALVIN, S. B. (1947). Complement-fixation studies in experimental

histoplasmosis. Proc. Soc. exp. Biol., N. Y. 66, 342-345.
SALVIN, S.B. (1952). Endotoxin in pathogenic fungi. J. Immunol. 69, 89-99.
SALVIN, S. B. & HOTTLE, G. A. (1948). Factors influencing histoplasmin formation. J. Bact. 56, 541-546.
SAMPSON, K. & WESTERN, J. H. (1954). Diseases of British grasses and herbage legumes. London: Cambridge University Press. pp. 131.
SÁNCHEZ BOTIJA, R. (1951). Contribución al conocimiento de las micosis gástricas. An. Fac. Vet. Madrid 3, 341-350.
SARKISOV, A. K. (1954). Mycotoxicoses. Moscow: Sel'khozgiz. pp. 216.
SAUNDERS, L. Z. (1948a). Cutaneous blastomycosis in the dog. A case report. N. Amer. Vet. 29, 650-652.
SAUNDERS, L. Z. (1948b). Systemic fungous infections in animals: a review. Cornell Vet. 38, 213-238.
SAUNDERS, L. Z. (1955). Fungous diseases. [In Hull, T. G., Diseases transmitted from animals to man, 4th Edit. pp. 433-463. Springfield, Ill.: Charles C. Thomas.]
SAUNDERS, P. T. (1914). Epizootic lymphangitis or Erysipelas and thrush on horse. Pamphl. Ser. Dep. Agric. W. Ind. No. 77, pp. 13.
SAUTTER, J. H., STEELE, D. S. & HENRY, J. F. (1955). Aspergillosis in a cat. J. Amer. vet. med. Ass. 127, 518-519.
SCHELLNER. (1935). Ueber eine beim Pferde durch Hefezellen verursachte Geschwulst in der Nasenhöhle und deren Nebenhöhlen. Z. Veterinärk. 47, 111-116.
SCHERR, G. H. (1953a). Enhanced dissemination of moniliasis in mice by the injection of yeast. J. Creighton Univ. Sch. Med. 8, 20-24.
SCHERR, G. H. (1953b). The effect of environmental temperature on the course of systemic moniliasis in mice. Mycologia 45, 359-363.
SCHIEBLICH, M. (1921). Mykose der serösen Auskleidung der Leibeshöhle bei einer Taube verursacht durch Aspergillus flavescens. Berl. tierärztl. Wschr. 37, 76-77.
SCHLEGEL, M. (1912). Soorkrankheit bei Hühnern. Münch. tierärztl. Wschr. 56, 63.
SCHLEGEL, M. (1921). VII. Soorkrankheit bei Gänsen. Z. InfektKr. Haustiere 21, 204.
SCHNEIDER, W. (1954). Favusepidemie durch Feldmäuse. Hautarzt 5, 348-351.
SCHÖPPLER, H. (1919). Pneumonomycosis aspergillina Leporis cuniculi L. Zbl. Bakt. 82, 559-564.
SCHROETER, H. & STRASSBERGER, L. (1931). Cholin als Schadstoff in kranker Gerste. Biochem. Z. 232, 452-458. (Cited by Steyn, 1933.)
SCHWABE, C. W. (1954). Present knowledge of the systemic mycoses in dogs: a review. Vet. Med. 49, 479-486 & 490.
SCHWARTE, L. H., BIESTER, H. E. & MURRAY, C. (1937). A disease of horses caused by feeding moldy corn. J. Amer. vet. med. Ass. 90, 76-85.
SCOTT, H. H. (1925). A streptothrix disease of wallabies. Proc. zool. Soc. Lond. 1925, 799-814.
SCOTT, H. H. (1928). Report on the deaths occurring in the Society's Gardens during the year 1927. Proc. zool. Soc. Lond. 1928, 81-119.
SCOTT, H. H. (1930). Tuberculosis in man and lower animals. A study in comparative pathology. Spec. Rep. Ser. med. Res. Coun., Lond. No. 149. pp. 270.
SCULLY, J. P. & KLIGMAN, A. M. (1951). Coincident infection of human and

anthropoid with Microsporum audouini; report of a case. Arch.Derm. Syph., Chicago 64, 495-498.
SEDDON, H. R. (1929). Mycotic dermatitis of sheep. Vet. Res. Rep. N. S. W. 1927-28, 5, 10-18.
SEDDON, H. R. (1953). Diseases of domestic animals in Australia. Part 5. Bacterial diseases. Vol. II. Department of Health, Commonwealth of Australia, Service Publication (Division of Veterinary Hygiene) No. 10.
SEEHAWER. (1934). Mykologische Untersuchungen über die im Hoppegarten beobachtete Trichophytie der Rennpferde. Z. Veterinärk. 46, 180-194.
SEELE & LAUER. (1955). Sprosspilze als Krankheitserreger, insbesondere im Eutergewebe bei Kühen. Mh. Tierheilk. 7, 94-102.
SÉGRETAIN, G., VERGE, J., DRIEUX, H., MARIAT, F., PARAF, A., LABIE, C. & THÉRON, B. (1956). Mammite à "Cryptococcus neoformans". Bull. Acad. vét. Fr. 29, 33-41.
SEIBOLD, H. R., ROBERTS, C. S. & JORDAN, E. M. (1953). Cryptococcosis in a dog. J. Amer. vet. med. Ass. 122, 213-215.
SELIGMANN, E. (1952). Virulence enhancing activities of aureomycin on Candida albicans. Proc. Soc. exp. Biol., N. Y. 79, 481-484.
SELLERS, K.C., SINCLAIR, W.B.V. & LA TOUCHE, C.J. (1956). Preliminary observations on natural and experimental ringworm in cattle. Vet. Rec. 68, 729-732.
SFORZA, M. (1946). Segnalazione di mastiti da Asteroides e prove di pastorizzazione del latte inquinato con tali germi. Boll. Soc. ital. Med. Sez. Eritrea 6, 153-159.
SHAHAN, M. S. (1937). A dermatomycosis of guinea-pigs. Arch. Derm. Syph., Chicago 36, 335-341.
SHEATHER, A. L. (1920). Bovine lymphangitis. J. comp. Path. 33, 158-185.
SHORTT, H.E. (1923). The pathogenicity of insect flagellates to vertebrates, with special reference to Herpetomonas ctenocephali, Fantham. Indian J. med. Res. 10, 908-933.
SILVA, M. & BENHAM, R. W. (1952). Nutritional studies of dermatophytes with special reference to Trichophyton megnini Blanchard 1896 and Trichophyton gallinae (Megnin 1881) comb. nov. J. invest Derm. 18, 453-472.
SILVA, M. E. & PAULA, L. A. (1956). Infecção natural de ratos pelo Histoplasma capsulatum na cidade do Salvador, Bahía. Bot. Fund. Gonçalo Moniz 9, 1-17.
SIMMONS, G. C. (1955). Mycotic dermatitis. Aust. vet. J. 31, 296.
SIMON, J. (1955). In vitro inhibition of mixed strains of Cryptococcus neoformans isolated from cattle. Amer. J. vet. Res. 16, 394-396.
SIMON, J. & HALL, R. (1955). An outbreak of bovine mycotic mastitis associated with dry storage of teat cup inflations. J. Milk Tech. 18, 298-299.
SIMON, J., NICHOLS, R. E. & MORSE, E. V. (1953). An outbreak of bovine cryptococcosis. J. Amer. vet. med. Ass. 122, 31-35.
SIMPSON, C. F. & WEST, E. (1952). Ergot poisoning in cattle. Circ. Fla agric. Exp. Sta. No. S-43. pp. 6.
SINCLAIR, J. M. (1921). Rep. Chief vet. Surg. South. Rhod. 1920, 6.
SINGH, S. (1956). Equine cryptococcosis (epizootic lymphangitis). Indian vet. J. 32, 260-270.
ŠIPKA, M. (1957). Candida tropicalis kao uzročnik mastita kod krava.

[Candida tropicalis as the cause of bovine mastitis.] Vet. Glasn. 11, 747-751. [In Croat.]

SIPPEL, W. L., BURNSIDE, J. E. & ATWOOD, M. B. (1954). A disease of swine and cattle caused by eating moldy corn. Proc. 90th Ann. Meet. Amer. vet. med. Ass. 174-181.

SKINNER, C. E. (1947). The yeast-like fungi: Candida and Brettanomyces. Bact. Rev. 11, 227-274.

SKINNER, C. E., EMMONS, C. W. & TSUCHIYA, H. M. (1947). Henrici's "Molds, yeasts, and actinomycetes". 2nd Edit. New York: John Wiley & Sons Inc.

SKULSKI, G. & SYMMERS, W. St. C. (1954). Actinomycosis and torulosis in the ferret (Mustela furo L.) J. comp. Path. 64, 306-311.

SLACK, J.M., SPEARS, R.G., SNODGRASS, W.G. & KUCHLER, R.J. (1955). Studies with microaerophilic actinomycetes. II. Serological groups as determined by the reciprocal agglutinin adsorption technique. J. Bact. 70, 400-404.

SLADEN, W.J.L. & AUSTWICK, P.K.C. (1955). The mycoflora of wild pink-footed geese sampled in Iceland and Scotland, 1953. 7th Ann. Rep. Wildfowl Trust, 1953-54, 133-138.

SMIT, H. J. (1915). Aspergillosis bei einem Huhn und einem Kaninchen. (Cited by Tomppert, 1940.)

SMITH, C.E. (1943). Coccidioidomycosis. Med. Clin. N. Amer. 27, 790-808.

SMITH, D.L.T., FISCHER, J.B. & BARNUM, D.A. (1955). Generalized Cryptococcus neoformans infection in a dog. Canad. med. Ass. J. 72, 18-20.

SMITH, H. (1934). Two cases of actinomycotic mastitis. J. Amer. vet. med. Ass. 84, 635-644.

SMITH, H. (1948). Coccidioidomycosis in animals with report of a new case in a dog. Amer. J. Path. 24, 223-233.

SMITH, T. (1920). Mycosis of the bovine fetal membranes due to a mould of the genus Mucor. J. exp. Med. 31, 115-122.

SMITH, W.W., MENGES, R.W. & GEORG, L.K. (1957). Ecology of ringworm fungi on commensal rats from rural premises in southwestern Georgia. Amer. J. trop. Med. Hyg. 6, 81-85.

SNIJDERS, A.S. & JANSEN, B.C. (1955). A comparison of Streptothrix bovis and Actinomyces dermatonomus. Bull. epiz. Dis. Afr. 3, 242-243.

SOLIMAN, K. N. & ROLLINSON, D. H. L. (1951). Mycotic infection of the skin of the turkey. Vet. Rec. 63, 20-24.

SOMMER, A. F. & BUCHANAN, A. R. (1955). Effects of ergot alkaloids on pregnancy and lactation in the albino rat. Amer. J. Physiol. 180, 296-300.

SPRING, A. (1848). Sur une Mucédinée développée dans la poche aérienne abdominale d'un pluvier doré. Bull. Acad. Belg. Cl. Sci. 15, 486-491.

STABLEFORTH, W. (1937). Cutaneous streptothricosis. A case in Great Britain. Proc. R. Soc. Med. 30, 1455-1457.

STAHMANN, M. A., HUEBNER, C. F. & LINK, K. P. (1941). Studies on the hemorrhagic sweet clover disease. V. Identification and synthesis of the hemorrhagic agent. J. biol. Chem. 138, 513-527.

STAZZI, P. (1905). L'aspergillosi nasale nel cane. Clin. vet. Milano 28, 193-199. (Cited by Romanov, 1928.)

STEELE-BODGER, A. (1953). Bovine mastitis due to yeasts. Vet. Rec. 65, 304.

STEYN, D. G. (1933). Fungi in relation to health in man and animal. Onderstepoort J. vet. Sci. 1, 183-212.

STORY, L. F. (1952). Bluestone absorbed by wool affects processing. N. Z. J. Agric. 85, 501-503.

STUART, P. (1951). An outbreak of bovine mastitis from which yeasts were isolated, and attempts to reproduce the conditions experimentally. Vet. Rec. 63, 314.

SYMEONIDIS, A. & EMMONS, C. W. (1955). Granulomatous growth induced in mice by Absidia corymbifera. Arch. Path. 60, 251-258.

TAKOS, M.J. & ELTON, N.W. (1953). Spontaneous cryptococcosis of marmoset monkeys in Panama. Arch. Path. 55, 403-407.

TALICE, R.-V. (1932). Parasitisme des hérissons par les Mycotorulées. Ann. Parasit. hum. comp. 10, 81-84.

TAPPI, V. (1952-53). Contributo allo studio dell'eziologia dell'enteroepatite infettiva dei gallinacei. Ann. Fac. Med. vet. Torino 3, 243-263.

TEVIS, L., Jr. (1956). Additional records of Haplosporangium parvum in mammals in Britain. Nature, Lond. 177, 437.

THARY & LUCET, A. (1895). Mycose aspergillaire chez le cheval. Rec. Méd. vét. Ser. 2. 8, 337-343.

THEILER, A. (1927). Die Diplodiosis der Rinder und Schafe in Süd-Afrika. Dtsch. tierärztl. Wschr. 35, 395-399. (Cited by Steyn, 1933.)

THIRY, G. (1913). Muguet spontané chez le singe. Arch. Parasit., Paris 16, 168-176.

THJØTTA, T. (1933). Pneumomykose som dødsårsak hos hare. Norsk VetTidsskr. 45, 275-279.

THOM, C. (1928). Yeasts and molds of milk and milk products. pp. 386-401 in Rogers, L. A. Fundamentals of Dairy Science. pp. 543. Monogr. Ser. Amer. Chem. Soc.

THOM, C. & RAPER, K. B. (1945). A manual of the aspergilli. pp. 373. Baltimore: Williams & Wilkins.

THOMPSON, L. (1950). Isolation and comparison of actinomyces from human and bovine infections. Proc. Mayo Clin. 25, 81-86.

THOMSON, R. E. M (1954). A species of Rhizobium isolated from strawberry foot-rot in sheep. J. Path. Bact. 68, 445-452.

THOMSON, R. E. M. & BISSET, K. A. (1957). Polysepta: a new genus and sub-order of bacteria. Nature, Lond. 179, 590-591.

THOROLD, P. W. (1951). Equine sporotrichosis. J. S. Afr. vet. med. Ass. 22, 81-83.

THOROLD, P. W. (1953). Equine dermatomycosis in Kenya caused by Microsporum gypseum. Vet. Rec. 65, 280

THORP, F., Jr. (1938). Further observations on oat hay poisoning. J. Amer. vet. med. Ass. 92, 159-170.

TICHOMIROV, D.M. & BOGDANOVIC, S.B. (1941). Einige pathologisch-anatomische und pathologisch-histologische Veränderungen bei Ratten, die mit Ustilago maydis vergiftet wurden. Frankfurt. Z. Path. 55, 7-13.

TITSWORTH, E. H. & GRUNBERG, E. (1950). A medium for the growth and maintenance of the yeast-like phase of Histoplasma capsulatum. Mycologia 42, 298-300.

TOMLINSON, W. J. & GROCOTT, R. G. (1945). Canine Histoplasmosis. A pathologic study of the three reported cases and the first case found in the Canal Zone. Amer. J. clin. Path. 15, 501-507.

TOMPPERT, H. (1940). Die durch Schimmelpilze verursachten Erkrankungen unserer Haustiere. Inaug. Diss., Hanover.

TORRES, G. & GEORG, L. K. (1956). A human case of Trichophyton gallinae infection. Disease contracted from chickens. Arch. Derm. Syph.,

Chicago 74, 191-197.

TRUCHE, C. (1926). Mycose chez la poule. Bull. Soc. cent. Méd. vét. 79, 370-375.

TSCHERNIAK, W. (1924). Beitrag zur Histologie der Lungenknötchen bei Pferden. (Vorläufige Mitteilung.) Z. InfektKr. Haustiere 25, 140-143.

TSCHERNIAK, W. S. (1928). Zur Lehre von den Broncho- und Pneumonomykosen der Pferde. Arch. wiss. prakt. Tierheilk. 57, 417-444.

TSCHERNIAK, W. S. (1934). Die Schimmelpilzmykose des Magens bei Schweinen. Z. InfektKr. Haustiere 45, 72-80.

TUCKER, E. W. (1954). Case reports on yeast infections of the bovine udder. Cornell Vet. 44, 79-85.

TUCKER, R. & MILLAR, R. (1953). Outbreak of nocardiosis in marsupials in the Brisbane Botanical Gardens. J. comp. Path. 63, 143-146.

TURN, J. & EVELETH, D. F. (1954). Coccidioidomycosis in a North Dakota cottontail rabbit (Sylvitagus floridaurus). Proc. N. Dak. Acad. Sci. 8, 42-43.

van UDEN, N. & do CARMO SOUSA, L. (1957). Yeasts from the bovine caecum. J. gen. Microbiol. 16, 385-395.

van UDEN, N., de MATOS FAIA, M. & ASSIS-LOPES, L. (1956). Isolation of Candida albicans from vegetable sources. J. gen. Microbiol. 15, 151-153.

van ULSEN, F. W. (1955). Schimmelabortus bij runderen. Tijdschr. Diergeneesk. 80, 1081-1088.

UNDERWOOD, P. C. (1955). Detection of crop mycosis (moniliasis) in chickens and turkey poults with a panendoscope. J. Amer. vet. med. Ass. 127, 229-231.

URBAIN, A. & GUILLOT, G. (1938). Les aspergilloses aviaires. Rev. Path. comp. 38, 929-955.

UTSI, M. N. P. (1956). Sixth Annual Report of the Reindeer Council of the United Kingdom, 1954-55. pp. 44.

VANBREUSEGHEM, R. (1950). Position systématique et nomenclature de l'Achorion quinckeanum. Ann. Parasit. hum. comp. 25, 188-199.

VAWTER, L. R. (1946). Pulmonary actinomycosis in swine. J. Amer. vet. med. Ass. 109, 198-203.

VERGE, M. J. (1927). Les aspergilloses des oiseaux. Rec. Méd. vét. 103, 521-528.

VERON, H. A. (1933). Diseases of Sheep, p. 257. Sydney: The Author.

VERTINSKIĬ, K. I. (1940). [Food poisoning in horses due to Stachybotrys alternans.] Sovyet. Vet. No. 5. pp. 61-68. [In Russian.]

VILANOVA, X. & CASANOVAS, M. (1951). Observations cliniques et mycologiques sur une épidémie de trichophytie transmise du lapin à l'homme. Pr. méd. 59, 1760-1762.

VINK, H. H. (1941). Mucormycose bij een varken. Tijdschr. Diergeneesk. 68, 312-315.

VÖLKER, R. (1924). Pneumomycosis aspergillina bei jungen Gänsen. Dtsch. tierärztl. Wschr. 32, 580-583.

VOGEL, R.A., FETTER, B. F., CONANT, N. F. & LOWE, E.P. (1954). Preliminary studies on artificial active immunization of guinea pigs against respiratory challenge with Coccidioides immitis. Amer. Rev. Tuberc. 70, 498-503.

VORONOV, D.L. (1949). [Seasonal spread and modes of infection in epizootic lymphangitis.] Veterinariya, Moscow 26, No. 9. pp. 23-25. [In Russian.]

VRŸBURG, M. A. (1907). Une espèce particulière de farcin du boeuf

sévissant en Deli (Sumatra). Rec.Méd.vét. 84, 31-39;171-177;241-248.
VUILLEMIN, P. (1901). Les blastomycètes pathogènes. Rev. gén. Sci. pur. appl. 12, 732-751.
WAKSMAN, S.A. & HENRICI, A.T. (1943). The nomenclature and classification of the actinomycetes. J. Bact. 46, 337-341.
WALKER, J. (1915). Aspergillosis in the ostrich chick. Rep. Dir. vet. Res. S. Rhod. 3-4, 535-574. (Cited by Urbain & Guillot, 1938.)
WALKER, J. (1930). Aids to stockowners. Dep.Agric. (Div.Vet.Res.) Kenya. Nairobi, pp. 159.
WALKER, J.I.J. (1955). Possible infection of man by indirect transmission of Trichophyton discoides. Brit. med. J. ii, 1430-1431.
WALKIEWICZ, W. (1934). Grzybica żołądka u świń. Wiad. weteryn. 13, 449-463. [In Polish.]
WATERS, R. (1932). Mycotic dermatitis in sheep. N. Z. J. Sci. Tech. 13, 309-310.
WATKINS, C. V. (1940). Some remarks on two diseases affecting the lungs and air-sacs in poultry. Vet. J. 96, 207-210.
WATSON, E. A. (1920). A note on equine sporotrichosis. Canad. vet. Rec. 1, 18-19.
WEIDLICH, N. (1952). Aspergillusabort und -Hautkrankheit bei einem Rinderfötus. Dtsch. tierärztl. Wschr. 59, 279-280.
WEIDMAN, F. D. (1935). Arch. Derm. Syph., Chicago 31, 64-65.
WEIDMAN, F. D. & RATCLIFFE, H. L. (1934). Extensive generalized torulosis in a cheetah or hunting leopard (Cynaelurus jubatus). Arch. Path. 18, 362-369.
WELLS, C. W. (1955). Federation of Malaya. Report on the Veterinary Department for the year 1954, [Kuala Lumpur: Govt. Press 52 pp.] p. 13.
WENDT, D. O. (1941). Sporotrichosis in a jack. Vet. Med. 36, 321.
WESTON, W.A.R.D. & HALNAN, E. T. (1927). "Black spot" of eggs. Poult. Sci. 6, 251-258.
WHITE, W. L., MANDELS, G. R. & SIU, R. G. H. (1950). Fungi in relation to the degradation of woollen fabrics. Mycologia 42, 199-223.
WICKERHAM, L.J. (1951). Taxonomy of yeasts. Tech. Bull. U.S. Dep. Agric., No. 1029. pp. 56.
WILSON, C. D. (1957). (Personal communication.)
WYSSMANN, E. (1941). Über Aspergillosen beim Rind. Schweiz. Arch. Tierheilk. 83, 166-171.
YOUNG, A. M. (1956). Chronic diffuse ringworm due to Microsporum canis in a dog, involving two claws. Vet. Rec. 68, 606-607.
ZEIDBERG, L. D. (1954). A theory to explain the geographic variations in the prevalence of histoplasmin sensitivity. Amer. J. trop. Med. Hyg. 3, 1057-1065.
ZEIDBERG, L.D., AJELLO, L., DILLON, A. & RUNYON, L.C. (1952). Isolation of Histoplasma capsulatum from soil. Amer. J. publ. Hlth 42, 930-935.
ZLOTNIK, I. (1955). Cutaneous streptothricosis in cattle. Vet. Rec. 67, 613-614.
ZSCHOKKE, E. (1913). Ein Rhinosporidium beim Pferde. Schweiz. Arch. Tierheilk. 55, 641-650.
ZÜRN, A. (1876). Beiträge zur Lehre von den durch Pilze hervorgerufenen Krankheiten der Hausthiere. Arch. Wiss. prakt. Thierheilk. 2, 110-114.

ZÜRN, A. (1877). Eine ansteckende Euterkrankheit bei Kühen. Dtsch. Z. Tiermed. 3, 381-387.

ZYCHA, H. (1935). Mucorineae. Kryptogamenflora der Mark Brandenburg und angrenzender Gebiete. Vol. 6a. pp. 264. Leipzig: Verlag von Gebrüder Borntraeger.

INDEX

Index